COVID-19 and Mental Health

How a Global Pandemic Affected our Psychological Well-being

TABLE OF CONTENTS

Introduction

- Why this book?

Chapter 1 Learn the Basics

- The Wuhan epidemy
- The outbreak
- What is coronavirus?
- How deadly?
- COVID-19 and Mental Health

Chapter 2 Mental Health

- Mental Health: What is it?
- Why is mental health just as important?
- What is a mental disorder?
- How to preserve your mental health

Chapter 3 The Science

- Transmission
- Influence of DNA
- Digital test proofs
- Emotional recognition accuracy
- Vaccine and immunity

Chapter 4 The Positive

- Hygiene
- Health check
- Innovations
- Reduction in crime rate
- More utilisation of media

Chapter 5 The Negative

- Malnutrition
- Poor health care
- Unhealthy living
- Low income
- Border closure
- Isolation
- Stigmatization
- Death
- Spread of fake news

Chapter 6 The Psychology

- Fear and anxiety
- Depression
- Post-traumatic stress
- Aggression

INTRODUCTION

For some time now, issues related to mental health have gained attention. But so many years of neglect have forced society to make even more efforts to ensure the awareness that the issue deserves.

The corona pandemic had a major impact on people's mental health and quality of life.

Stress was almost inevitable when the current corona crisis started. This applied to patients and the general practitioner's team.

Anxiety, concern and uncertainty about one's health or that of a loved one are normal.

Research showed that people currently had considerably more anxiety and depression during the corona crisis than before. Most people will recover on their own, some won't.

Sometimes normal stress reactions turn into more serious psychological complaints.

Why this book?

It is often difficult for people in time of crises. Uncertainties, panic, anxiety, depression, death, cancelling appointments and having to stay home can cause extra stress.

It is therefore important that people are informed as well as possible about how these circumstances can influence their mental health and total wellbeing.

Therefore, considering the obvious damage that neglecting mental health can have on people and the consequent losses to the labour market, I present this book titled "Covid-19 and Mental Health."

I'll take you through the beginning of the covid crises to the effect it had on the mental health of people.

That's what this book gives to you: information.

I'll discuss the science, positive, negative and psychological effect of the covid pandemic on your mental health.

It's a long ride, let's start!

CHAPTER 1

Learn the Basics

Almost 1.7 billion people in the world (22% of the world's population) have at least one disease that can lead to serious complications when infected with the coronavirus.

The first wave of infection of the coronavirus seems to be over in most countries. However, that doesn't mean we can just resume our old lives.

What exactly is this virus, how deadly is it, what are the symptoms and how can it affect our mental health?

In this book, you will find your answer.

Let's begin!

The Wuhan epidemy

An unanswered question.

This has remained the definition of the origin of the covid-19 pandemic since it was first detected in the Chinese city of Wuhan about a year and a half ago.

Coronaviruses are common cold viruses. But there are also special forms. For example, SARS and MERS are both diseases caused by coronavirus.

Many scientists argue that the virus was probably transmitted from an animal to a human. Then the virus mutated and became transmissible from person to person.

A lot has been said again that the virus may have come out of a laboratory.

Specifically, from the Wuhan Institute of Virology.

The first case of the new coronavirus pandemic, SARS-CoV2, was identified in Wuhan, China, on December 31, 2019.

Since then, cases began to spread rapidly around the world: first across the Asian continent, and then to other countries.

In February, the transmission of Covid-19, the name given to the disease caused by SARS-CoV2, in Iran and Italy drew attention to the rapid growth of new cases and deaths, causing the Ministry of Health to change the definition of suspected cases to include patients who have been to other countries.

In March, the World Health Organization (WHO) defined the outbreak of the disease as a pandemic.

The outbreak

In late December 2019, the World Health Organization (WHO) received the first warnings from Wuhan, a city in China's Hubei province, about the number of people living with pneumonia. The virus these people were infected with was later identified as a novel coronavirus, COVID-19 (previously referred to as 2019-nCoV).

This organism belongs to a family of viruses, which include the common cold, as well as SARS and MERS viruses.

SARS (Severe Acute Respiratory Syndrome, caused by SARS-CoV);

> originated in China;
> an outbreak in 2003;
> affected approximately 8,000 individuals worldwide.

MERS (Middle East Respiratory Syndrome, caused by MERS-CoV);

> an outbreak in 2012;
> mainly affected people in the Middle East.

Covid-19 (Corona Virus Disease, caused by SARS-CoV-2);

> originated in Wuhan, China, late 2019;
> a global outbreak in 2020.

At the end of January 2020, it was determined that more than 7,000 people had been infected by the virus. The WHO has indicated that China was the worst affected country at the time. Outside of China, a smaller number of cases were reported from Hong Kong, Macau, Japan, Korea, Vietnam, Singapore, Australia, Malaysia, Cambodia, Philippines, Thailand, Nepal, Sri Lanka, India, United States, Canada, France, Finland, Germany, United Kingdom and the UAE.

The severity of 2019-nCoV was investigated through the CDC (Centers for Disease Control and Prevention) and the WHO. On January 30, the outbreak was declared a public health emergency.

What is coronavirus?

COVID-19 or Coronavirus Infection is an infectious disease caused by the most recently discovered coronavirus.

It is caused by an infection with SARS-CoV-2, a coronavirus.

The coronavirus belongs to the virus family.

Many people think that a virus is about the same as a bacteria (both small and scratchy), but that comparison is wrong. A bacterium is essentially still a small animal, while a virus is no more than a wrapped string of genetic material, with the inscription: COPY ME.

This 'copy order' allows the virus to read the body into which it has entered, as it were, in the hope that cells will carry out that order. The virus is the size of one ten-thousandth of a millimetre.

How deadly?

Doubt is being cast from various quarters about the seriousness and lethality of Covid-19. According to some, it is all not too bad: more than

90% of patients also survive among the over-85s. If you're under 70, your survival rate is a whopping 99.95%. Is this true and how many deaths does the virus really make?

What makes Covid -19 different than, say, the flu, which after all also makes you sick?

In one word: unpredictability.

So much is unknown about the virus that containment is the only option for the time being.

We don't know for sure how deadly the disease is. Because there are still seriously ill in hospital, and because there are probably many patients without or with mild symptoms that are not in the statistics. The 'pie' of infected patients is then larger, so the percentage of deaths is smaller.

Anyway, because the chance that you will die if you are infected does not say much about the total number of victims that a virus can cause. Very few people infected by the flu die from it, yet this disease kills hundreds of thousands of people every year. At least as important as the risk of death is the contagiousness of a virus.

Interpreting the covid-19-related death rates is not easy. The most reliable measure is excess mortality. We compare the mortality of the past year with the mortality of previous years. Significantly more people died in 2020 than the average in the previous five years. It's not just about old people with other illnesses. Healthy older and younger patients can also die from Covid-19. The numbers would probably have been much higher if heavy measures were not taken.

Covid and mental health

The pandemic caused by SARS-CoV-2, the virus that causes the disease COVID-19, has caused unprecedented human, economic and social damage. Therefore, it is a particular stressful condition that impacts our minds, disrupts economies and increases the risk of developing mental disorders.

In public health terms used in a mental health context, the main psychological consequences of a pandemic today are heightened stress and anxiety. At the same time, as new anti-epidemic measures and related changes are introduced (first of all, quarantine, which affects people's usual activities, everyday life and basic sources of livelihood), the prevalence of loneliness, depression, harmful use of alcohol and alcohol consumption may also increase as well as the prevalence of self-harm or suicidal behaviour.

The global economy, the complex networks of international relations, individual mental health, the ups and downs of everyday life: nothing was spared during the pandemic.

When we think of covid-19, however, "trauma" may not be the first thing that comes to mind, let alone "collective trauma".

Other references—economic, psychological, ecological, scientific—may seem more appropriate.

And even within the mental health field, "trauma" is not often the preferred topic in media discussions, which focus more on other issues such as depression, anxiety, loneliness and stress.

Trauma is a much more subtle concept than most of us realize. It's not just a word for something extremely stressful. Trauma is about events and their effects on the mind.

There is no health without mental health. To be in good health is, therefore, to be in good physical and mental health: we all have mental health. Good mental health enables individuals to achieve fulfilment, overcome normal stresses in life, do productive work and contribute to collective life. In this positive sense, mental health is the foundation of an individual's well-being and the proper functioning of society.

I've broken down the history of the covid virus so you can understand, let's dive into mental health and then we will look into the science, positive, negative and psychological effects of covid on you and your mental health.

Ready?

CHAPTER 2

Mental Health

Mental health is the health of your mind. When you think of health, you quickly think of your body, your condition, your physical health.

The mental health of the world has been compromised since the start of the Covid-19 pandemic.

Therefore, it is natural that this situation impacts our lives causing more stress, anxiety, insecurity, sadness, among other feelings caused by social isolation and uncertainty about the disease.

Even with the arrival of the vaccine, it is still important that we don't forget to take care of our bodies, increasing immunity and preventing the spread of the virus. Care with distance, mask use, hand hygiene and everything that comes into contact with the world outside the home needs to be redoubled. However, we also have to remember to take care of our minds in this difficult time.

A study showed that there was a deterioration in the mental health of the population because of its repercussions (confinement, isolation, loss of employment, etc.).

Mental health: what is it?

According to the World Health Organization, "mental health is not just about not having an illness, it is about feeling good."

Mental health is the dimension of our health that concerns our feelings. We have the health of the heart, vessels, skin, intestine and we also have the health of our feelings, of our connection to the world. Therefore, to have good mental health is to be happy, or at least not to be unhappy.

When the mental health is good, the feelings, the emotions are pleasant, even if we can have small fears, stress that can arise, that we will know how to overcome or not.

Why is mental health just as important?

Normally, we think of the body and mind as if these two entities were separate from each other. With this, many people see medicine as an area that only takes care of physical health, without taking into account the mental state.

Comprehensive health care is essential. From it, we can see that the mind is part of the body, as it originates in the various synapses of our neurons. Injuries and changes in these cells can cause psychiatric illness.

Likewise, our sense of well-being influences the entire body.

Why does it happen?

Our entire body is monitored and controlled by the nervous system. The main information about our functioning is transmitted by neurons. They release substances called neurotransmitters to communicate with each other and with other cells, especially those in the endocrine and immune systems.

All of this is what's called neuroimmunoendocrine integration.

Nothing happens in our body without our nervous system, which also includes the brain, which is nothing more than our mind. The bodily functions are integrated by billions of neurons, releasing neurotransmitters that receive information about metabolism and the external environment, and send commands to other organs.

Taking care of the body, therefore, is also taking care of the mind—and vice versa.

Mental health is just as important as physical health because a healthy mind also makes you stronger physically. That means you get off the couch more easily and have more meaning in life. Of course, everyone feels gloomy, anxious or tired from time to time. That's completely normal and part of it.

What is a mental disorder?

A mental disorder is a disorder of brain activity that can affect an individual's mood, behaviour, reasoning, way of learning and communication.

As they do not have clear physical symptoms, mental disorders have been ignored for many years during the history of medicine and have only been studied in depth in recent decades.

Common types of mental disorders

The most common types of mental disorders are:

- Depression: a clinical condition characterized by lasting sadness and loss of interest in daily activities;
- Anxiety disorder: fear, worry, or excessive agitation characterize this disorder;
- Bipolar disorder: mood changes that alternate moments of depression with symptoms of obsession (mania);
- Dementia: group of symptoms manifested in behaviour and social interactions;
- Attention deficit disorder: difficulty in attention or concentration, hyperactivity and impulsive behaviour;
- Schizophrenia: a disorder that affects a person's sensitivity and ability to interact with others;
- Obsessive-compulsive disorder: thoughts that lead to repetitive behaviours;

- Post-traumatic stress: occurs after a situation of loss or danger, when a person lives or witnesses a frightening episode. It can result in waves of anxiety or a panic attack at triggers that remind the individual of the situation.

How to improve your mental health

Turn your worrying thoughts into positive thoughts.

Worrying about anything and everything: everyone does it once in a while. Especially now. Our thoughts have a huge influence on how we feel. Therefore, make it a habit to speak kindly and positively to yourself. It can help to write down positive things about your day every day or to make a list of beautiful things in life. Positivity attracts positivity. Really!

Bring structure to your life.

Do you sometimes feel like you're running ahead of yourself? There are only 24 hours in a day and you can't do everything. Create order in your head by setting priorities and put them on paper. You do this by making a daily schedule or to-do list. Do not plan your days too full and stick to fixed rhythms. Every day at the same time at the table and at the same time to bed? That helps to create a healthy pattern in your life.

Make time for fun things.

We are constantly working to achieve our goals. There's nothing wrong with that, but it should also be fun. Make sure you have a good balance between your daily obligations and relaxing activities. Did you want to do sports, but did you choose to go to the movies for an evening? There's nothing wrong with that at all! Take the time to relax and plan a fun activity each week with friends or family. So you always have something to look forward to

Regularly plan a day of nothing and get enough sleep.

If you find that it's all getting too much for you, take a step back. It's not easy to say no to an appointment, but you don't want to be exhausted. It's okay to do nothing for a day regularly. In addition, getting enough sleep is very important for your mental health. Therefore, make sure you get enough sleep every day; that is 7 to 8 hours per night for adults (although that can vary per person).

Healthy food.

Eating healthy is not only important to keep your body strong, but it also helps you to feel good mentally. Good nutrients such as fibre, antioxidants and vitamins give your body and mind energy throughout the day. Do you find healthy eating difficult? Do it in small steps. Replace a bowl of chips with unsalted nuts. Or a cookie for a banana. Easy!

Talk about your feelings.

Are you not feeling okay? Nothing to be ashamed of! Talking about it with a family member or friend can give you a lot of relief. If you find it difficult to indicate what you need, ask for help. Are you stuck? You can also look for a solution together with your doctor.

Sports.

People who exercise are less likely to have psychological complaints than people who do not exercise. If you exercise 1 to 3 hours a week, you have a 1.5 times smaller chance of developing a psychological disorder. Reason enough to take your sports shoes out of the closet again?

Be a little selfish.

Think about yourself. What makes you good? What makes you wrong? Bring only positivity into your life. Allow yourself to do something that brings you happiness often.

Keep toxic people, unsolvable problems, and excessive worry away. Don't feel bad about distancing yourself.

It is popularly said that taking care of you is an act of selfishness, but in reality, it is an act of love.

Only you know what's best for yourself. If you feel the need to disconnect from everyone and everything, do so for a few hours or a weekend.

Slowing down doesn't mean ignoring your problems and being distracted by more pleasurable activities.

This is called procrastination.

Slowing down is finding the best possible way to deal with the complications of everyday life so as not to affect your mental and physical health.

Let's dive into the science, positive, negative and psychological effects of covid on you and your mental health.

Ready?

CHAPTER 3

The Science

The global outbreak of the coronavirus and the measures taken by the government to contain it have a major impact on our society.

Much attention in healthcare is of course to prevent the spread of the virus. But due to the strict measures, people also died lonely and that should have been prevented by also looking at the scientific aspects of this corona crisis.

In the beginning, therefore, too little attention was paid to the non-health effect of the corona crisis, such as the innovations it made possible, transmission, and influence on our DNA.

Transmission

How is it possible in many cases that when someone contracts the coronavirus, their family members do not become infected?

A study was carried out to research how the transmission of the coronavirus within families works. To this end, the antibodies in the blood of some families were studied.

Unnoticed antibodies

Through serological testing, it was determined whether other family members have developed coronavirus antibodies.

If this was the case, this means that they have possibly contracted the coronavirus in the past – possibly without knowing it. As a result, important questions can be answered. For example, how well these people are protected against contracting the coronavirus again, and whether they react differently to the vaccine. The extent to which older family members infect younger ones, and vice versa, was also be studied.

Looking for answers in our DNA

Some participants were intensively monitored since the start of the coronavirus pandemic. A survey was sent out 19 times, including the question of whether people experienced symptoms that could align with a coronavirus infection. Together with the data from the serological testing, this information provided new insights into transmission within households.

Spots were found in DNA that could lead to people experiencing more severe coronavirus symptoms faster after being infected, so there could also be spots in DNA that ensure that people are protected against contracting the coronavirus or experiencing severe symptoms.

Influence of DNA

Because the world became more self-reliant during the coronavirus pandemic, the extent to which DNA influences their behaviour and wellbeing became greater.

The researchers discovered that people who had a different genetic predisposition handled the coronavirus pandemic differently.

People with a higher genetic predisposition for neurotic behaviour, for example, displayed anxiety around vaccinations more often, and a genetic predisposition for feelings of depression had an effect on reported fatigue over the past year.

People with a genetic predisposition for high educational attainment also shook hands with others less frequently, but also washed their hands less frequently.

In addition, it appears that people with a genetic predisposition for alcohol consumption experienced difficulty with avoiding food and drink venues. And even though people didn't go skiing or snowboarding, the people who had planned to do so in November were more likely to have a genetic predisposition for risk-taking.

Digital test proofs

These digital Covid-19 test results can be used in the future for access control of events. This allows events to be organized where, for example, the 1.5-meter rule can be dropped because all visitors have tested negative for Covid-19 just before the event.

This is a new step to be able to open up society further and to offer perspectives to sectors that suffer greatly from the restrictions.

The developed solution makes it possible to link a Covid-19 test result to the identity of a person. This person stores this data in a personal data safe on his telephone. The test result with linked identity can then be easily displayed at the access control of the event. The digital test result can be validated in real-time by the organizer for authenticity.

With this solution, events and large-scale meetings can be made possible again by allowing visitors to show these digital test results.

Emotion recognition accuracy

Protective face masks have become omnipresent in public life. People wear them when grocery shopping, when sitting on the bus, and when interacting with others at their work. While the medical benefits of face masks are clear, whether and how face masks influence the dynamics of our interactions with others is only poorly understood.

Many people feel that face masks make it harder to know what others are feeling, or whether others can be trusted. But is this actually true?

An online experiment in which they presented participants with portrait photographs of individuals expressing various emotions. For half of the participants, parts of the presented faces were covered by a face mask. Once a photograph was presented, participants indicated what emotion the person expressed and how they perceived the person.

'Reading' emotions

The study confirmed that face masks indeed make it harder to accurately 'read' others emotions. Face masks also make others appear less close, possibly leading people to move closer – a counterproductive response that undermines virus containment measures.

Surprising effects were found when masked faces expressed negative emotions: Masked persons who express anger, sadness, or disgust were seen as more trustworthy, likeable, and less distant compared to people not wearing face masks.

A positive consequence may be that distressed people wearing a face mask may be more likely to receive assistance from others when needed.

Consequences

Overall, face masks undoubtedly shape people's everyday interactions. They influence the accuracy with which they recognize emotions as well as their social judgements. Hence, people, politicians, and policymakers should be mindful of face masks' consequences above and beyond the medical context.

Vaccination and immunity

Vaccine researchers have acted extraordinarily fast, under extraordinary pressure. With the brunt of global expectations, they delivered safe and effective vaccines that had been rigorously tested in trials.

But with that comes some important caveats. The extent of protection depends on the vaccine - in some cases, there is not yet enough data to be sure.

Until you get a booster dose and many more people are vaccinated, it is vital that you continue to socialize, wear a mask, and follow other public health advice. In fact, it helps to imagine that this did not happen.

Collective immunity is a kind of resistance to disease that manifests itself in a population, following the build-up of immunity in individuals. But unlike the impression you might have had during the pandemic, there are several reasons why it is not normally achieved by intentionally letting a virus spread. Many scientists now believe that any such attempt would have resulted in an unacceptable number of deaths. But group immunity can also be acquired through vaccines, which cause much less collateral damage and may offer greater protection against natural infections.

That said, the current Covid-19 vaccines have not been evaluated on their ability to prevent the spread of the virus, but rather on their ability to prevent people from developing symptoms and getting sick. Research to determine whether vaccines also prevent transmission of the virus is still ongoing, but some preliminary indications show that some vaccines may reduce transmission. There are early signs that other vaccines may be able to stop it completely.

CHAPTER 4

The Positive

The virus made its appearance when all kinds of major bottlenecks were felt, both in public health and in healthcare and the living environment. This marked a turning point for the world.

For example, the corona crisis has contributed to the accelerated development of changes in our healthcare and society. Awareness of the importance of good accessible care and the appreciation of healthcare staff has increased significantly. The application of digital technologies has accelerated enormously, while in recent years it has struggled with slow implementation. We can also point to a stronger mutual connection in the district and neighborhood, the willingness for far-reaching intensive collaborations in the region. People experience more peace and attention to a healthy lifestyle seems to have increased, which increases support for prevention.

Amid this scenario, the impacts of the coronavirus on HR were gigantic. After all, the sector is primarily responsible for driving decisions and changes together with the organization's leaders.

The effects are also enormous. On top of these are the possible consequences of innovations, reduction in crime rates and more utilization of media.

Let's dive more into it.

Hygiene

Hygiene in the world is now at the top of the agenda.

People are more conscious of their hygiene than before.

The cleaning industry around the world has been forced to adapt faster than ever due to the Covid-19 outbreak, as cleaning and hygiene are high on the agenda as a means of combating the spread of the virus.

As companies are slowly allowing their employees to return to the workplace after months of working from home, there is a clear focus on implementing cleaning solutions for a healthy work environment.

Health check

Understandably, in the first phase of the corona crisis, a lot of attention was paid to the health of COVID-19 patients and the care they needed.

The crisis has made future challenges for public health and cares even more urgent. Corona puts a magnifying glass on the vulnerabilities and problems, as it were.

The urgency of continued cooperation between ministries

The corona crisis has led to more intensive cooperation between the ministries. This interdepartmental collaboration also offers opportunities in the longer term to further improve public health. After all, many targets lie outside the health domain. Think of work and labour, education, the physical living environment and social security.

In short: the urgency to work together on a healthier country, across the ministries, is once again underlined by the corona crisis.

Adaptation to remote work

Remote work was already gaining ground in the market, but many companies were not yet adept at the model. With the pandemic, the home office became the ideal option to avoid agglomerations, forcing organizations to reinvent their way of operating.

But how can you turn the key so suddenly without dropping productivity? One of the most important steps is to create a teleworking policy with clear guidelines.

Once this is done, hold a meeting with all employees explaining the home-office rules and make it clear to everyone how the model works, what are the responsibilities of each one and what are the expectations in relation to deliveries and results.

It is also essential to provide all the necessary tools for professionals to perform their functions, such as a corporate cell phone and notebook, as well as a complete home-office kit to meet the needs of teams working at a distance.

Innovations

One of the biggest impacts of coronavirus on the world is the need to implement technological resources to manage teams from a distance. The point of registration, for example, needs to be adapted utilizing geolocation applications, biometric validation or facial recognition.

The technology in the cloud is another great ally in the pandemic. With it, it is possible to access documents using any device connected to the internet, making it possible to send medical certificates, share files and manage tasks, among other daily activities.

Changes in recruitment and selection

Selection processes also benefit from the use of technology during the home office. Applications of videoconferencing, for example, can be used to conduct virtual interviews without the need for personal contact between candidates and recruiters.

Some platforms make it possible to apply tests and other steps remotely, allowing 100% online recruitment. Even sending personal documents for admission can be done virtually, making the process easier and eliminating bureaucracy.

Increase in layoffs

With the crisis, many companies suffered from reduced sales, contract freezes and lost customers, needing to lay off employees to balance the bills.

This was one of the biggest impacts of the coronavirus on the world, as the sector is responsible for helping to decide who will be hacked and conducting all shutdown processes.

Effects can be felt in numbers. According to the Ministry of Economy, more than 1.5 million formal workers were laid off between March and April, the first two months of the pandemic in the country. The figure represents an increase of 31% over the same period in 2019.

At this point, it is essential to put in place measures for responsible dismissals, such as extending benefits, offering career advice and referring terminated employees to other companies.

A real example of this practice is Uber, a giant in transport applications that had to lay off about 3,000 employees because of the crisis. Due to the moment, the company decided to pay another ten weeks of salaries to all those fired, in addition to maintaining health plans until the end of the year.

Remember that the entire process must be carried out with respect and transparency, communicating the news to each employee in individual conversations. Never make the mistake of firing someone in a group video call or with an email/WhatsApp message.

Need for distance training

Having teams in quarantine or at home-office mean that in-person training must be cancelled indefinitely. However, this does not mean that the training of employees should be interrupted.

As well as in daily activities and selection processes, it is also possible to insert technology into employee development, using videoconferences, gamification, multimedia content and other tools.

These new training models were already being implemented by many companies to increase the participation of teams. The trend is that, even after the pandemic, they continue to grow and become permanent.

The growing importance of feedbacks

In this moment of distancing, feedbacks are even more important for the employee to feel that their work is seen and recognized. In addition, it is an interesting way to bring the leaders of your teams together and make HR remembered by everyone in the company.

So don't let go of structured feedbacks. On the contrary, do your best to adapt them to this new reality and make them a useful tool for evaluating employee performance and increasing productivity.

How to stay positive

Covid-19 has a major impact on our daily lives. The impact is great when you, your family or your acquaintances get sick. But even if you are not infected, the coronavirus has a major impact on your life. There are many things that we cannot do in these times, but there are also plenty of things that we can do. You must focus on what can be done during this time!

Healthy eating, staying mentally fit and getting enough exercise is extra important at this time. Try to live as healthy as possible, because then your immune system works best. This way you give the coronavirus less chance of hitting hard. 'Staying healthy' goes beyond not getting sick. In these times you have to take good care of yourself.

1. Keep moving

In these times it is important to take good care of your body and to exercise regularly. Because exercise not only keeps your body healthy but also your head. Sufficient exercise ensures better concentration and better mental health. But how do you ensure that you move enough (inside) in these times? You do that by challenging yourself! You can move in all kinds of ways, such as a walk, a home workout or an online yoga session. Always make sure you keep enough distance.

2. Eat healthy and enough

Being at home all day and working from home can mess up your daily routine. This can have a major impact on your diet. Sleeping, exercise and healthy eating contribute to optimal resistance. Your body has a better defence against pathogenic bacteria and viruses and you are less likely to get sick when your resistance is optimal. For example, try to get more healthy snacks at home to resist temptations, make vitamin-rich smoothies and try out new healthy recipes.

3. Stay mentally healthy

You quickly think of your body, condition and physical when you think of health. But taking care of your mind is just as important. When you are comfortable in your skin and also in your head, you are more positive in life, you function better, you suffer less from stress and you can deal with problems better. We are currently living in an uncertain time due to corona. You may be worried about your job and your income. Or maybe you are concerned about your health or the health of others. This can lead to tension and uncertainty and give stress and insomnia. Take care of yourself and maintain good mental fitness and try to reduce or prevent stress.

4. Stay in touch

Even though we have contact with each other differently due to the virus, it is very important to have a nice network around you, so you stay positive in these times. It is very important to keep in touch with others. How do you take care of this now? Call up old(er) people and have a chat. How are they? Do they need help?

This is a win-win situation because helping others has a positive effect on you as well as on the person you are helping. Today's technologies help with this. Always stay in touch with your family and friends, (video) call them regularly and ask how you are doing!

5. Keep busy!

And finally, keep busy with daily things and do what makes you happy! This way you stay positive and healthy. Plan your day with time for school/work, shopping, etc., but also plan some time for moments of rest and to do the things that make you happy and get your energy from. This ensures that you have a moment of relaxation and discharge every day and it helps you stay positive. Also think about small, happy moments in your day. Is the sun shining today? Does the garden look nice? How does your cup of coffee taste? Precisely these small moments of enjoyment can already give you a positive feeling.

CHAPTER 5

The Negative

According to the World Health Organization, "mental health is not just about not having an illness, it is about feeling good ".

Mental health is the dimension of our health that concerns our feelings. We have the health of the heart, vessels, skin, intestine and we also have the health of our feelings, of our connection to the world. Therefore to have good mental health is to be happy, or at least not to be unhappy.

However, the health crisis linked to Covid-19 and the restrictive measures taken as a result has had a negative impact on the mental health of the world.

Due to the ease of contagion, the main guideline to curb the spread of the virus is social isolation, which has had a labour impact on the labour market.

As a result, many companies around the world have had to temporarily close their doors, reduce their operations or implement the home office, which has significantly altered their day-to-day workflow.

The pandemic leads to unemployment, lower household incomes and, through disruptions in supply chains, reduced availability of food rich in essential nutrients.

Malnutrition

For us it is clear: for children worldwide, the end of this pandemic cannot come soon enough. The quality of life of millions of children has declined for decades in almost every area, from education to feeding.

Malnutrition is a result of a lack of nutrients. For example proteins, carbohydrates, fats, minerals and vitamins. This leads to unwanted weight loss and poorer functioning of the body. It occurs mainly in the elderly and the sick, but sometimes also in children.

Nearly seven million children were likely to have become acutely malnourished last year, meaning an additional 10,000 children per month could die from malnutrition.

Acute malnutrition is a life-threatening condition, leaving children 3 to 12 times more likely to die than children of healthy body weight.

Malnutrition at a young age leads to negative consequences that are not only very serious but also irreversible. A diet that does not contain all the necessary nutrients has serious lifelong consequences, such as delays in neurocognitive development, a lower level of education, and later a low-paying job; other consequences include an increased risk of chronic disease and premature death.

These problems ultimately affect society as a whole, as the malnourished children of today will be less creative, innovative, and productive as adults tomorrow.

Causes

Malnutrition can have various causes. Illness is one of the biggest culprits. When you're sick, your body may need more nutrients. It costs your body a lot of energy to fight against the disease. In such a time it is sometimes important to get a little more food so that a normal diet is no longer sufficient. The following factors may play a role in malnutrition:

- Decreased appetite or nausea
- Psychological complaints (e.g. anxiety, depression or sadness) that cause your appetite to decrease
- Social factors such as loneliness, or not being able to buy or prepare food
- Dementia
- Addiction
- Having trouble chewing, tasting, swallowing or digesting
- Reduced absorption of nutrients, for example, due to intestinal diseases or burns

Effect

Malnutrition has major consequences for the body and health.

Consequences include:

- Slower recovery after surgery or illness,
- More and more serious complications after surgery,
- Delayed wound healing,
- Increased risk of pressure sores (decubitus),
- Reduced functioning of the immune system,
- Decreased muscle mass (decrease in strength),
- Reduced heart and lung capacity,
- Lower quality of life (less zest for life),
- Increased risk of death.
- In growing children, malnutrition can cause serious permanent damage.

Symptoms

How do you recognize malnutrition? There are several symptoms that may be associated with malnutrition:

- Reducing muscle mass
- Decreased appetite

- listlessness
- Thin and dry skin
- Fatigue
- Decrease of fatty tissue under the skin
- Feeling cold often
- Dry hair
- Reducing heart and lung capacity
- Impaired immune system function
- Increased risk of pressure sores
- Slow wound healing

Slower recovery, more and more serious complications after surgery

Lower quality of life, for example, due to depression

What can you do about malnutrition?

Do you suspect that you or someone close to you suffers from malnutrition? Then it is good to contact a doctor. Your doctor can help you get enough nutrients back in a healthy way. Your doctor can also help you with a referral to a dietician or other professional. Below I have listed the important factors regarding malnutrition for you:

1. Eat healthily: check whether you eat a varied and sufficient diet.

2. Arrive healthily: gaining weight in a healthy way differs per person. One may lack other nutrients compared to another. Therefore, enlist the help of a dietician or other professional. However, you can take the following into account: eat and drink more fatty products. For example, drink whole milk instead of semi-skimmed milk and eat an avocado instead of mango. Also, have a handful of nuts as a snack.

3. Pay attention to meals: stick to fixed times when you eat something. In any case, make sure you help to make food tasty and cozy, that makes it a bit easier to keep up.

4. Make it easy on yourself: choose food that is easy to prepare or have a hot meal delivered to your home if necessary. That way it can reduce the burden of eating.

5. Make sure you exercise enough: this will make you feel fitter and increase your appetite. For example, a brisk walk can do you good!

6. Stop smoking: it is not only much better for your health, but it also improves your taste, which may make you find food more enjoyable and tastier.

Poor health care

Understand why the existence of a public health system, to which any citizen can have access, contributes at a time of health crisis with the Covid-19.

The new coronavirus pandemic has changed social relationships around the world. Social isolation has transformed how people relate and the daily lives of the entire population. With this, the concern and alert for mental health care became constant.

Good health care is often a problem, especially in rural areas in developing countries.

In many countries, healthcare is not what it should be. Due to lack of knowledge, it is difficult to prevent diseases. The population often knows little about hygiene, access to sanitary facilities is poor and hospitals also lack good hygiene. The transmission of diseases is therefore very common.

Causes

1. Low investments

Expenditures remained the same, but the amount that came in was smaller — only a small per cent of the state budget — causing the health system to break down and making it even more difficult to improve public health.

In addition, the inefficient financial administration and the irregular transfer of budgets affect the quality of work, as they tend to prioritize medium and high complexity units, such as hospitals, instead of investing in primary care.

In other words, even with low funding, one way to overcome the public spending challenge is to organize the state budget. A larger amount should be transferred to primary care, for investments in health units, family care strategies, psychosocial care centres and health posts. This way, it will be possible to avoid the big occupations in hospitals.

2. Alarming diseases

It is necessary to keep in mind that the challenges are constantly interconnected. Low investments are not only reflected in the overcrowding of hospitals, but also in the increase of alarming diseases, lack of professionals, poor infrastructure, etc.

We constantly see news reporting new epidemiological crises and outbreaks, especially of diseases that had disappeared, such as measles and yellow fever. We are experiencing an example of this situation with the worldwide infection by COVID-19.

Other relevant clinical issues

Another worrying issue is the strong movement of the population against vaccines in recent years, mainly due to the fear of developing pathologies from them. This caused the appearance of diseases, as well as the return of others that, until then, had been eradicated.

Rumours also emerged about adverse reactions or diseases that vaccines could cause, such as paralysis of the lower limbs, autism, etc., which were vehemently refuted by the scientific community.

In this way, the work of public professionals (both at the entrance door and in the secretariats) had to be redoubled to handle the care of long-standing illnesses. They also have the role of preventing the increase in mortality, constantly changing management and performance.

3. Lack of public health professionals

One of the most popular courses in the world is Medicine, but, for some reason, there are few professionals in public health. Analyzing the points already mentioned, it is no surprise that doctors, nurses and technicians opt for the private clinic, even leaving public tenders aside.

After all, few people want to work in a place that constantly requires changes to deal with re-emerging pathologies, high work hours, extended shifts, poor infrastructure and, above all, low wages.

In addition, although there are professionals interested in working in the network, poor distribution emerges to further complicate the situation. Doctors are redirected to places that do not need their services, such as some capitals, which causes the neglect of other cities.

As I mentioned, one problem is always related to another. In this sense, the lack of doctors and nurses in hospitals or health facilities ends up generating overcrowding and long waiting lists.

With the entry of the coronavirus, health professionals in the three levels of care are suffering from an overload of physical and mental stress, which will hinder assistance for those who need it.

4. Overcrowding in hospitals

One of the pillars of health is the right to care for everyone — the reality, however, is not quite that. Although almost 70% of the population does not have a private health plan, highly complex units are overwhelmed by the lack of professionals and quality equipment, while primary care networks have long waiting lines.

This not only discourages professionals but also reduces the quality of care, as demand is not reduced throughout the day. With the rise of alarming pathologies, the chance of developing hospital infections increases, generating even more stress and difficulty for the team — and, of course, among the patients.

This is the reality that health authorities want to avoid with the arrival of the coronavirus, as hospital spread was identified by studies published by the Chinese as the main cause of the increase in cases of COVID-19. As soon as social distancing and monitoring of patients at home began, the incidence of new cases decreased.

5. Outdated infrastructure

As well as the lack of specialized professionals, other major challenges are the low infrastructure and poor quality of equipment available. If workers' motivation was already reduced due to overcrowding and the high workload, the outdated infrastructure only aggravates the situation.

Thus, fewer and fewer doctors and nurses want to work in the public system, opting for private clinics. The management responsible for the quality of equipment and materials also has flaws, causing more discomfort in daily life and reducing the level of public health.

With the entry of the coronavirus, the obsolescence of equipment and the insufficient quantity will be even greater challenges to reduce the epidemic curve and bring normalcy to citizens.

6. Low-quality technology

Technology came to revolutionize human life. Everywhere, we can find people who work with the internet, use social networks, invest in entertainment and improve their business techniques. When applied to health, technological resources bring several benefits, such as:

- Development of equipment with advanced technology;
- Decrease in invasive procedures;
- Increased diagnostic accuracy;

- Ease in understanding prognoses;
- Improvement of management and administration techniques.

It turns out that, with the low investment in public health, cutting-edge technology cannot be experienced by the population — these benefits are only applicable to private clinics. In addition, the incentive to train the team is reduced, making it difficult to correctly use technological equipment and, consequently, intensifying the precariousness of the public health system.

This panorama is also a result of the low investments in health as previously reported and will worsen if the coronavirus epidemic reaches gigantic levels.

Faced with all these challenges, how to develop quality public health that meets the needs of the population, values your team and has good management? The first step is to invest in primary care, exploring the gateway units and then working with medium and high complexities.

The coronavirus epidemic has exposed a complicated situation in the already complex public health system. Even in the face of globally recognized public programs, we still suffer from low technology, poor infrastructure, unmotivated professionals and, now, physically and emotionally overloaded due to COVID 19 infection. I hope that the pandemic will serve as a lesson for managers and others involved with human health.

Unhealthy living

Does lifestyle determine how vulnerable you are in a pandemic?

Yes.

An unhealthy lifestyle increases the risk of chronic conditions and makes you more vulnerable. For example, overweight people often suffer from diabetes and cardiovascular diseases: all risk factors for a bad course if you get COVID-19.

If you are fit, your immune system works better and that makes you less vulnerable in a pandemic.

The effect of an unhealthy lifestyle

The body needs to get healthy food. When the body does not get the daily necessary nutrients, this can have major consequences for the body and health. Food is bad for the body if it contains few or no nutrients. This is also known as empty food. When empty food is consumed, the brain receives a signal that the stomach is full, but the body can only extract few nutrients from it. An example of empty food is instant noodles. This product contains so few nutrients and on the other hand too many preservatives, that it would even be bad for your health.

Another form of bad nutrition is the fat people that are known to everyone, namely fast food. Fast food can indeed contain good nutrients, but they are almost always present in the wrong amounts. A large hamburger can contain almost half the recommended daily amount of calories. And the short-term effects of poor nutrition can greatly affect life. This can manifest itself in stressful situations, a bad mood and persistent fatigue. Research has shown that long-term stress from poor nutrition also affects the body. So much so that permanent damage can occur.

In the long term, there are also consequences for an unhealthy lifestyle, namely obesity, high blood pressure, diabetes, cardiovascular disease and depression.

Towards a healthy lifestyle

The very first step to a healthy lifestyle is to adapt to a healthy diet. Healthy food provides enough energy and nutrients for the body and consists of sufficient proteins, carbohydrates, fats, vitamins, minerals, fibre and moisture. By adapting nutrition, the body will not only become fitter but also reduces the risk of diseases such as diabetes and cardiovascular disease. It is therefore recommended to eat enough vegetables and fruit, lots of whole grain products, fatty fish once a week, few sweet drinks containing sugar and little red or processed meat.

In addition to a healthy diet, it is also important for a healthy lifestyle that there is an active exercise for at least half an hour a day at least five days a week. This can be, for example, brisk walking, cycling, swimming or dancing. This movement does not have to be for half an hour in a row, but can also be spread over the day. It has been proven that regular exercise is healthy and that the body gets fitter over time. The muscles, lungs, heart and blood vessels will get used to moving a lot.

Nutrients that contribute to a healthy lifestyle

Nutrients can contribute to a healthy lifestyle. Sometimes it is possible that a body with a healthy diet does not get the recommended daily amount of vitamins and minerals. Then extra nutrients can be a possible supplement in daily life.

Factors such as unhealthy diet, medicines, UV radiation, environmental pollution, alcohol and smoking can adversely affect the skin. To limit these influences, the body needs antioxidants that are obtained from foods. Supplementing your diet with an antioxidant supplement is a good choice so that these influences are limited.

Low income

Millions of families have lost their income as a result of the crisis and are struggling to survive.

Covid-19 not only causes health problems, for many people it also has financial consequences. Financial stress can be both a cause and effect of ill health.

For many people, the corona pandemic means a drop in their income. That makes them financially vulnerable. Financial vulnerability and (physical and mental) health are intertwined.

This can lead to a vicious circle: financial stress can be both a cause and consequence of ill health. In addition, financially vulnerable people often have no access to healthcare. Or they can't afford it, and they may stop taking medication. This is especially worrying during the current health crisis.

Tips for your income

1. List your monthly income

Start with a list of your income per month. This includes your wages, benefits or pension. Also, consider arrangements such as child benefits and allowances. Do you receive a provisional refund from the tax authorities? Please include it in your overview.

2. Do the same with your expenses

Divide your expenses into your fixed expenses and your daily expenses. Your fixed costs are, for example, your housing costs, energy and subscriptions. These are expenses that you cannot simply cut back on and that usually come back monthly. Daily expenses are for example groceries, transport and eating out.

3. Make a budget

Divide all your expenses into categories. Determine an amount per category how much you spend on average per month. Create a budget entry for each category.

4. See if you can save

Once you have everything in order, you can see where you have room to make changes to your expenses. See if you can save on fixed costs by, for example, taking out cheaper subscriptions or taking out cheaper insurance. Look carefully at where the money goes for your daily expenses. Are all expenses necessary, or can you cut some expenses?

5. Set a savings goal

Determine how much you will save each month. If you use an internet savings account, set up an automatic transfer to your savings account. If you don't need money for a longer period, consider other options for building wealth.

Border closure

The COVID-19 pandemic has triggered border controls in many countries around the world to curb the spread of the disease. These measures halted progress towards economic integration. Trade restrictions put in place in response to the pandemic are fueling fears of a new food crisis on the continent.

Border controls linked to the pandemic are having numerous economic repercussions. Here we examine these impacts and suggest ways to mitigate the cost to local communities.

Most countries have policies in place to close borders. This particularly concerns land borders. While freight can pass under tight control conditions not only at customs posts but also along internal trade corridors, people can no longer do so.

Freight movement permits are sometimes granted only for agricultural and food products.

Virtually all of these countries have suspended the arrival of international flights, at least from countries particularly affected by the virus. In many countries, these measures have been accompanied by a curfew.

People entering at border posts are subject to temperature control and testing, followed by hospitalization and/or quarantine if necessary.

These measures were taken for health purposes, but their economic consequences could be significant. More health controls at the borders on the transport of products are expected to slow intra trade. In addition, prohibiting people from crossing the border stops informal trade in small quantities, an activity widely practised in the world.

It is often the essential source of income for a family. This trade represents a significant share of recorded trade.

Effect

It remains difficult to systematically answer this question. The lack of recent data makes it difficult to get the big picture.

The decisions to close the borders were adopted without apparently a precise knowledge of what was happening on the ground. Thus, in some countries, due to the heat in broad daylight, fresh and perishable products are usually transported at night. Curfews make this practice impossible.

More in-depth health checks, without reinforcing the administrative teams, also increase transport times. These additional delays and curfews could imply waste and loss of products.

Banning individuals from crossing a border can be particularly costly for pastoralists. Beyond the cost to trade for mature animals, it is the mode of operation of pastoral agriculture that is threatened.

The slowdown in trade and the ban on border crossings for individuals can also make it more difficult to access certain inputs such as fertilizers or pesticides.

The implementation of exceptional measures provides fertile ground for abuse of power.

In some regions, it is customary for law enforcement to set up 'checkpoints' along trade corridors to take bribes. As recent measures taken have slowed down the number of road transportations, this predatory behaviour has increased in intensity.

Most of these measures were not subject to prior information. The effects of surprise on the local populations were numerous. When individuals have little possibility of finding other means of subsistence than informal activity linked to trade, this lack of communication unnecessarily aggravates the effects on economic agents. This can mean the lack of income for many families over several consecutive days with devastating effects on poverty and food security.

In addition, international or regional coordination of political decisions has been very generally absent. Many curfews have thus been put in place, but often at different times between neighbouring countries, which has accentuated the negative effects.

Ultimately, these measures can interrupt or slow down international aid, whether food or medical.

Potential solutions

Social transfers are needed, especially for informal traders who are usually cross-border trade. But these social transfers are expensive and difficult to design. How to set up these transfers during a period of confinement (absence of possible digitization of payments in certain countries)? How to put in place measures that take into account the specific vulnerability?

The World Health Organization (WHO) is also very reserved on border crossing bans. This gives people incentives to cross them through places not covered by customs authorities, and therefore without health checks. And for the WHO, if a government anticipated that the announcement of a virus involved travel bans and trade restrictions against its citizens and businesses, it would lessen its incentives to disclose the existence of this virus.

On the contrary, authorization of border crossings allows for health checks and possible screening, possibly followed by quarantines and/or hospitalization. It improves public information, the distribution of protective equipment, access to water, soap and disinfection equipment.

Regarding the passage of individuals at border posts, the imposition of social distancing may decrease the likelihood of the virus spreading. This presupposes strengthening the teams of customs officers working at the borders, so as not to slow down cross-border trade too much.

Costs for farmers and transporters of agricultural and food products must be reduced. For example, we can question the value of curfews, the impact of which on the transport of perishable products is negative. In terms of trade policy, we can also recommend a reduction in import taxes on agricultural and food products weighing on intra trade to offset the increase in transport costs. A suspension of export bans on these same products should also be considered.

The border restriction measures should be announced in advance to the populations to allow them to adapt as well as possible. And the international coordination of these policies should be maximum, to allow the exchange of information on the spread of the virus and the measures put in place.

Finally, countries must not allow the pandemic to stop progress in economic integration.

Defining coherent health and economic policies in the face of a pandemic such as Covid-19 is a particularly complicated exercise. It already seems very difficult in rich countries which nevertheless have significant financial resources and strong institutions. It ly even more so in poor countries, where financial resources are very limited, and institutions are sometimes weak. Policies suitable for countries with strong institutions may become inappropriate, or even harmful, in countries with weak institutions. Thus, as we have seen, imposing more stringent health controls along trade corridors can increase predatory behaviour by local control authorities and worsen the situation accordingly.

Isolation

We are all staying at home as much as possible to slow down the spread of the new coronavirus.

Social habits disappear, but the need for human contact remains. What does that do to us?

Only go outside for the much-needed groceries or a walk. Those who can't work from home can go out. The rest are strongly advised to stay at home as much as possible. With these measures, the cabinet hopes to slow down the spread of the new coronavirus and thus spread the number of sick people over a larger period. Schools and catering were closed. Public transport was scaled back. People must stay one and a half meters away from each other: no shaking hands and no kisses and hugs. That's weird for a human. We don't know any better than to hang out in groups.

It is the first time since the Second World War that people have stayed indoors so en masse and have been thrown back on themselves. Until a few days ago, hardly anyone had any experience with self-quarantine. Separating ourselves from others is the best thing we can do for each other right now, but it goes against our needs. Will our mental health take a hit if we shut down for an extended period?

Connectivity online

As humans, we have a fundamental need for social connection. If this is not met, it can have consequences for our psychological health.

Loneliness is a predictor of depression.

Fortunately, loneliness is often a temporary feeling: it will pass. If you move to another city and don't know anyone, it's only natural that you feel lonely. Normally those feelings motivate us to do something about it, to get people around us. We actively look for it when we lack connection. And that, now that the coronavirus is around, is just not the intention.

Most people think that the consequences of this temporary self-quarantine for our mental well-being are not too bad. Yes, most people in society have fewer social contacts for a while, but that feeling of lack can be compensated for online, via (video) calling. People express the same amount of emotions online and are just as personal as they do face-to-face.

You used to sit at home during a war or pandemic and you had little contact with the outside world.

Now you can maintain contact online. I see it happening around me, that colleagues online compensate for the missed moments at the coffee machine.

Elderly hit hard

Anyone who thinks that health is the most important good for our well-being is wrong. Social relationships are more important.

The elderly are being hit extra hard by the virus. Firstly, they belong to the risk group of people who can become very ill. In addition, they already have an increased risk of becoming lonely.

Chronic loneliness is most common among people over 85. That harrowing feeling of loneliness is harmful: it causes just as great health problems as smoking, alcohol, being severely overweight and little exercise. The link with cardiovascular disease has often surfaced. The link with psychological complaints such as depression is even stronger.

The fact that the elderly are now allowed to receive few visitors and that clubs have been suspended makes it even harder for them.

The more time there is left to worry. It is precisely at times when you are worried that you need support from people who are close to you.

Alone but not lonely

Being temporarily thrown back on yourself does not have to mean that your well-being is going downhill quickly. Being alone is not necessarily lonely. The one is better alone than the other, so it will be among the inmates. The question is what do you do in this situation of social isolation. How do you interpret it? Do you experience a difference between what you have and what you lack, but do nothing about it? Or are you looking for compensation to make up for the lack in daily life?

Online there is a lot of advice from experts to deal with self-quarantine properly. Teams that are now forced to work from home try to mimic normal business. They do this in an unconventional way, such as with virtual drinks where everyone can call in to have a drink together. It's a good way to connect with others. It's weird, but everyone feels weird, that's what makes it fun.

Virtual parties bring some light to the difficult situation we are in.

Missing touch

You can see and speak to each other via telephone and computer. Touching each other is now out of the question.

How do we experience that lack?

Through skin contact, you produce the 'cuddle hormone' oxytocin, which makes you feel more comfortable. However, the effect of oxytocin in social contact is a bit overestimated. In studies, subjects are often given a large dose and then you see what happens. In reality, the effect is a lot more subtle.

In addition, there is still physical contact within a relationship or a family. Singles may miss touch more, but they probably had less of it anyway. I estimate that people will get over it if the measures last a few weeks. Does it take longer? Then the group that feels lonely runs the risk of psychological complaints.

Unrest and uncertainty

It is easy these days to feel stressed, anxious or depressed. Not long after the Chinese metropolis of Wuhan was cut off from the outside world and people were no longer allowed on the streets, the first signs of gloom and spiritual distress emerged. Four in ten people said they feel anxious about the virus. Telephone helplines have sprung up like mushrooms and offer mental support to people who are scared at home.

The virus is taking its mental toll. We're not just inside. We are inside with a headache.

The unrest and uncertainty surrounding the events complicate the consequences of social isolation. People are afraid of getting sick, making others sick, losing their jobs. There is a good chance that that uncertainty affects us more than staying at home.

Talking to the neighbours

For people with roommates and families, social abstinence is logically more sustainable. With a bit of luck, families will come out of isolation even closer.

The virus has strengthened my relationship with my wife and parents, now that I have been spending almost two months together in m house. My daughter is attracted to me more. I suddenly have the time to do the smaller things that I've always left. behind because of being busy.

I cook for my family and speaks to my neighbours again.

Whether you are forced to be at home on your own or are close to each other with a family, everyday life is undergoing major changes for everyone.

We all have social patterns that are strongly disrupted by the crisis. That's not necessarily a bad thing. What you often see is that people like to have some freedom. Social contacts take care of obligations. You always have to adapt to others. Being at home for a few days can be wonderful.

If it takes longer, it can naturally start to gnaw. For example, boredom sets in. There are no church services, no sports clubs, no dinners, card nights or birthday parties. You have to fill in the remaining time yourself.

I can imagine that sitting at home for a long time has consequences for your social network. You often see this when something drastic happens in someone's life. For example, if you are ill for a long time, friends will drop out. A select group remains.

Will the corona crisis also lead to a separation in our social network? Well, who knows. These are interesting times. Perhaps it is the other way around and people are now doing their best to maintain connections, we now find the peace of mind to call someone we never speak again. Perhaps we will see social cohesion return.

Stigmatization

Being weighed down by stigma, that's like being afraid with every contact that the other person will put an invisible label on your forehead. By prejudice or ignorance. Because you are secretly afraid that someone else will notice. Because you used that label yourself before. Do your colleagues, friends, family see you, or is their view directly disturbed by emotions and (pre)judgments that they associate with the label 'mentally ill'?

Stigma is a concept from sociology and means: a mark that distinguishes people from others. It attributes to them undesirable traits such as dangerous, unreliable or unpredictable behaviour. People or groups with a stigma are rejected, ignored or banned by others: we prefer to keep 'they' who are different from 'we' at a distance. Whether it concerns people who are infected with the virus, overweight, have a different sexual preference, a different skin colour or a psychological condition.

Process of exclusion

Stigmatization is the process by which people label, condemn and exclude a group with common and deviant characteristics and/or behaviours. This often happens through misunderstanding. The exclusion concerns, among other things, rights, obligations and participation in social activities. It may concern openly discriminatory behaviour or incorrect or incomplete knowledge and whether or not stereotypical views or prejudices. But also about 'under the hood', semiconscious views that determine the attitude of people towards someone with a mental illness or disease. It is precisely this unconsciousness that makes stigmatization such a persistent problem.

Prejudices

People with the coronavirus are often mistakenly believed to be dangerous and unpredictable. The assumption is that they cannot fulfil social roles well. Much of society believes that they are responsible for their condition and that the virus has a poor prognosis.

The perceived stigmatization is greatest among people with serious and long-lasting psychological disorders, such as persistent psychotic disorders, bipolar disorders and serious addictions.

Self-stigmatization

Self-stigmatization can occur when a person becomes part of a stigmatized group because he develops a mental illness or disease himself. Due to the bad image of the group, the newcomer expects to be rejected. This has a negative influence on his self-image, as a result of which he increasingly limits himself in his social functioning out of shame or fear. For example, people experience the consequences of stigma even without direct negative reactions from others.

Effect

A psychiatric stigma leads to major participation problems. It also violates the rights of people with disabilities.

Participation problems

The Coronavirus usually has negative consequences for a person's social identity and often results in structural disadvantage in several areas. Think of physical health, well-being, active citizenship and access to resources. People with the virus are often much less involved in normal life and therefore have fewer opportunities for an education, a job and a home.

(Self-)stigmatization can lead to symptoms of anxiety and depression, demoralization, social isolation, low self-esteem, low quality of life, demoralization and avoidance of professional help. The negative consequences of (self) stigma are also risk factors for suicide.

About half of people with the virus perceive stigmatization as the biggest barrier to their participation in society and the labour market. For this group, stigmatization is a daily source of concern. Social rejection is widely experienced, with the result that people with a (serious) illness or disease tend to undertake less and less (anticipated discrimination). Self-stigma reinforces this negative effect: for fear of being rejected, they stop looking for work or friendships and do nothing ('why try'). No wonder many choose to (selectively) hide their condition.

Tackling stigma

Self-stigma occurs in four parts:

- Putting yourself down: 'I often feel the least in company'. "I'm not going to that birthday party, people think I'm weird, so I'll be alone all night."
- Feeling yourself failing: 'I no longer count in society.' Or: 'There's no point in applying anymore, I don't have enough competencies anyway.'

- Your social withdrawal: 'I might as well stay at home, I can't connect with others anyway.'
- Fear of public stigma/low stigma-resilience: 'I'm afraid that people will no longer want to hang out with me if they hear that I'm being treated for the virus.' Or: 'People can see from me that I have the coronavirus.'

Understanding your stigmas and where your stigma counts most can help to dispel these preconceptions about yourself.

Not sure if you suffer from self-stigma? Take the test.

If you get a list of the thoughts that get in your way, you can work on this by finding out where these thoughts come from, so that you can discuss them. This also applies to emotion and behaviour. At what moments do you feel you are becoming small and what emotions does that produce. Do you avoid situations because of this? If you are afraid of the judgment of others, it may make sense to increase your resilience against prevailing stereotyping and prejudice. For example, by following a training, you may also be able to bring up self-stigma during your treatment or counselling.

Tips for negative thoughts

It is not easy to control self-stigmatizing thoughts. These can take on a life of their own. With self-stigma, but also with other negative thoughts, it is first of all important to be aware of these thoughts. Ask yourself where your thoughts come from. Know that thoughts can influence your behaviour. Ask for help if you feel you can't control your thoughts.

There are various therapies where you learn how to control your thoughts and what the effect is on your behaviour. Thoughts are also frequently discussed during training sessions and workshops in the field of self-stigma. Not to put them into perspective, but to make them negotiable.

Tips for negative emotions or feelings

No one is without emotions. Fortunately, because otherwise passion, compassion and love would not occur in our society. But emotions can also have a negative charge. Simply not going along with negative emotions or feelings is easier said than done.

Sometimes an emotion is demonstrable, you are sad when something bad happens. But what do you do when you are overcome with shame because you are afraid that you have done or said something strange. It is then useful to know where this emotion comes from. Ask yourself: Does it hinder me? If the answer is 'yes', then you can consider getting started with this.

Tips for withdrawing behaviour

"Just do it." If only it were that simple. With self-stigma, you often see that people start to avoid situations or activities out of fear of negative experiences or reactions. Most people know that avoiding is not very useful. It can cause you to become more and more out of the way, leaving you lonely or socially isolated. But simply picking up activities again is often not that easy. The first step is to recognize which situations you are avoiding. What thoughts go through your mind, what emotions do you experience. Don't trivialize your thoughts. Don't think 'well I never liked birthdays that much' when I actually do. Think about what you would like to pick up again.

Ask for help if you don't know where to start. That help does not necessarily have to come from a care provider. Ask someone you trust or an experienced expert who has studied the theme. And take the first step. Take action, but take it step by step. And then, in the end, it is: 'do it'.

Death

Approximately 152,000 people die annually in some countries (2019), of which 2,000 are younger than eighteen.

The number of surviving relatives is a multiple of this. About 1 in 5 next of kin has problems adjusting to the loss.

The pandemic brought a lot of deaths to our ears. Children lost parents, wives lost husbands and vice versa.

More than half of women over the age of 60 are left alone due to the death of their partner.

Every day many people are confronted with the death of a loved one. Such a loss is one of the most profound and saddest events in a person's life. From one moment to the next, the neighbour is permanently gone. That goodbye changes life forever. Even when it wasn't unexpected. Relatives, such as the partner, the parents and/or the children, are often overwhelmed not only by sadness but also by feelings of bewilderment, disbelief and/or anger. People say afterwards that they felt like they were going crazy or being numb. Death often comes as a shock to other family members, friends, colleagues, classmates and teachers.

Grieving process

During the grieving process, you gradually process the pain of the loss. You say goodbye and gradually accept the final absence of the beloved person. You try to adapt to the void that has arisen. Immediately after death, some people experience a sense of unreality. The death of the beloved seems like a bad dream, from which they soon wake up. Other people feel almost nothing, their feeling is, as it were, 'dead'. Still, others find the death of the loved one so painful that they first deny it. One person is completely devastated, the other reacts very calmly.

Confusing Feelings

Many relatives struggle with intense, confusing and sometimes contradictory feelings. Not only sadness, fear, helplessness and despair but also anger, aggression, disappointment and guilt can occur. Sometimes you feel relieved and in a way liberated. This is the case, for example, when death closes a long and difficult illness or when the sick person longed for the end. These unexpected feelings can be very confusing for those left behind, as they are perceived as inappropriate. However, they are normal reactions to a drastic change.

Lost zest for life

People who have lost a loved one often say that they have lost their zest for life or that life has lost all meaning. Some want to be with the deceased so badly that they start thinking about suicide. Only the responsibility for others prevents them from choosing death. These thoughts can be very frightening but usually disappear on their own over time.

Effects

- An intense feeling of being alone (with sadness).
- Emptiness, depression and not wanting to do anything.
- Guilt: Should I have done more, prevented his or her death?
- Increased alertness and restlessness or confusion and slow thinking.
- Can only think of the deceased.
- Many dreams about him or her.
- Like a movie always seeing the last hours or days.
- Thinking to see, hear or feel the deceased again.
- Look for him or her.
- Taking care of you worse and not eating right.
- Have less faith in yourself, the world or the future.

Tips

1. Take your time

Give yourself space and time to feel sadness, to be angry, to miss someone. You need that time to find and 'heal' a new balance. As time goes by, you will notice that memories become less painful.

2. Give emotions space

Everyone processes the loss of a loved one in their own way. So allow yourself to grieve in whatever way suits you: crying, laughing, relieved, or angry.

3. May your memories are there

You have shared years of your life with your loved one. This includes memories, photos, or objects that have special value to you. Think for yourself about what you want to do with this. Perhaps that will give you the strength to deal with the lack.

4. Take care of yourself

Grieving is hard work and takes a lot of energy. In order not to become completely exhausted, you need to eat well and get enough sleep. Try to relax now and then. For example, by doing something you enjoy: walking, picking up a hobby again or meeting up with friends.

5. Be open to others

Share your feelings with others and tell people what's on your mind. That often blows. Find someone you trust for that. This can be a family member, a good friend, or a doctor. Friends and neighbours may avoid you because they don't know what to say to you. They may find it difficult to cope with their feelings of loss. It can help if you take the first step. Show that you appreciate their friendship and support.

6. Find the help you need

It is sometimes difficult to share grief with family and friends. Especially if they think you're doing it 'wrong'. Then remember: there is no right or wrong way to deal with loss! If someone judges you for your feelings, he cannot help you. Don't be afraid to ask for professional help. It can point you in the right direction.

Spread of fake news

Due to the moment, everyone wants to be informed about pandemic data, government measures and other events that can influence their daily lives. But many people took advantage of this to spread false news and even apply scams, further increasing the fear and tension in the quarantine.

To preserve employees, disseminate content with tips for them to escape this type of trap and only inform themselves through reliable communication channels. A list of recommended sites and influencers were created, such as major news portals, scientists and health experts, among others to be the only sources of information.

CHAPTER 6

The Psychology

Amid the pandemic, there was much talk about measures to prevent Covid-19, but the mental health of employees cannot be overlooked either.

The situation created an environment of constant worry, instability and anxiety.

Many employees lived alone and were completely isolated from friends and family during quarantine, which caused an agonizing feeling of loneliness.

Therefore, it is interesting to know how to overcome some of the psychological effects it had on people.

Let's dive into the psychological effects of the covid virus on the mental health of people and how to overcome them to take care of our mental state in addition with tips to keep a healthy mind during this period.

Ready?

Fear and anxiety

As many as one in five people, consciously or unconsciously, suffered from an anxiety disorder or phobia during the covid crises. But what exactly is fear and what can you do about it?

What is fear?

You may now be wondering: what is fear? Fear is an emotion that helps you react to danger. The body goes into a state of alert, which causes the heart to beat faster, breathing faster, blood pressure rises and muscles tense. This sudden and intense fear often does not last long and everyone experiences it from time to time. It is a healthy response to imminent danger.

However, this healthy fear may become 'unhealthy' and you develop anxiety symptoms or even an anxiety disorder. People with an anxiety disorder are also afraid of situations that pose no immediate danger. For example, they panic when they have to give a presentation at work, don't dare go outside anymore or spend nights worrying. Anxiety disorders are in all cases serious symptoms that seriously affect the quality of life.

An anxiety disorder will eventually lead you to avoid ordinary situations. Fear controls your life in such a way that living a normal life is difficult. The consequences of an anxiety disorder can be serious, such as loneliness and alcohol abuse.

What is anxiety?

Experiencing fear in certain situations is therefore very normal, as long as that fear disappears after a certain time. Isn't that happening and are you (disproportionately) anxious most of the day or have you been regularly troubled by fear in harmless situations for a longer period? Then you may have an anxiety disorder.

In many cases, anxiety disorders start in childhood. Sometimes you grow out of it as a child, but you can also continue to suffer from it for years if your complaints remain untreated. The cause of an anxiety disorder varies from person to person.

Generalized Anxiety Disorder

If you are anxious and worried about everyday things all the time, you have Generalized Anxiety Disorder. It is very similar to depression, but with feelings of anxiety, such as sweating and palpitations. The difference with other anxiety disorders is that the fear is constant and not caused by a particular situation. This disorder usually starts later in life, between the ages of 50 and 60.

Symptoms

Your symptoms depend in part on the type of anxiety disorder. But these are common:

- Palpitations
- To sweat
- Hot flashes or chills
- Tremble or tremble
- Dizziness
- Breathlessness
- Chest pain
- Nausea, abdominal discomfort
- The feeling of unreality or of being detached from yourself
- Fear of going crazy or losing your temper
- Fear of dying
- Numb or tingling sensations

What to do with an anxiety disorder

An anxiety disorder rarely goes away on its own. Therefore, do not wait to seek help. The most important thing is that you admit that you have a problem and want to change it. You can work on your fears yourself and together with people around you (family, friends). For example with this self-help book or a course on the internet. You can also look for information and contact fellow sufferers via a patient organisation.

Do your complaints affect your daily life? Then go to your doctor, he can help you further.

People who suffer from an anxiety disorder for a long time can lose their work and friends and become lonely. The chance of this is especially high if they keep the fear hidden from everyone. Thirty per cent of people with an anxiety disorder also deal with depression or alcohol abuse. The fear is also often a heavy burden for a partner, children and friends. For example, if their friend never dares to walk down the street without their guidance.

Talk, but with whom?

It is important to share your problems with others. Talking air! By talking about your problems you are admitting to yourself that they are there. And maybe your complaints will become fewer. By thinking out loud you notice what kind of complaints you have and how bad they are. And you may find that you are not the only one with this problem. Perhaps this person can give you support. Many people don't dare to talk about their problems out of shame or fear of being considered 'crazy'. That fear is usually unfounded.

It is important to choose someone with whom you feel comfortable. Someone who knows you well and who cares about you. That can be a sister, brother or parent. But also a good friend or sports buddy. Sometimes problems are easier to discuss with someone you know less well. Think of a colleague, a confidential adviser or a company doctor.

Tips to overcome

- Try to get a good picture of your fear. And determine how this fear affects your life. For example, ask yourself the questions: What am I afraid of? What does this fear mean for my life?

- Talk about your fears with people around you, for example with family, friends or colleagues.
- Determine which complaints you have when you start to feel panic or anxiety. For example, ask yourself the questions: What do I feel when I start to panic or fear? What is happening in my body?
- Give in to the fear as little as possible. And confront yourself with the frightening situations for you. Do this in small steps.
- Realize that the panic will also pass.
- Be prepared for physical complaints that you get in frightening situations. Do you not run away from your complaints and do you face a confrontation? Then you notice that the restlessness, shaking and sweating subside after a while.

Depression

Depression is mainly characterized by a prolonged presence of depressed feelings and/or decreased interest or pleasure in almost everything you do. The causes and consequences of this differ per person. Research shows that about one in five people will experience depression at some point and the corona pandemic escalated it. This makes it one of the most common psychological problems in the world. Depression is most common in adults, but it can also affect children and young people.

Depression in children

Depression is not age-related. It is, therefore, possible that children will have to deal with it. In children, however, there is less of a persistent gloomy or depressed mood. Children often suffer from irritable or grumpy behaviour. However, this irritability should not be confused with irritability in response to frustration. It is true for these children that they have reduced interest and pleasure in things that they normally enjoy. In addition, they may also suffer from other depression symptoms that can occur in adults.

The difference between depression, grief and burnout

Having gloomy feelings, fatigue and not feeling like anything anymore are complaints that can also be related to other problems. These feelings can also be present in mourning and burnout. In grief, however, a feeling of emptiness and loss is at the forefront and the gloomy feelings diminish in intensity over time. In depression, other feelings come to the fore, namely sadness and the inability to imagine ever being happy again. In addition, the gloomy mood of depression is more persistent and not tied to specific thoughts, such as thoughts or memories of the deceased loved one. Burnout also has many similarities with depressive symptoms.

Symptoms

Depression can cause a variety of symptoms. Depression can seriously disrupt your normal life. At home, at work and in your free time. You usually have several complaints that last for a longer period.

If you are depressed, you have at least 1 of these symptoms:

- You feel gloomy and listless (almost) all day long.
- You are not or hardly interested in things that you otherwise enjoy.
- In addition, you may also suffer from depression:
- Concentration problems, for example, when reading or watching TV.
- Indecision: making decisions takes more effort, even on very small matters.
- Being sluggish and tired or restless and irritable.
- Feelings of guilt, or feelings of being superfluous and useless.
- Sleeping problems: sleeping badly or sleeping a lot.
- Loss of appetite: you do not feel like eating (and lose weight) or you eat extra (and gain weight).

- Blue Devils: You experience life as too heavy and can sometimes long for death.

Tips

There are several ways to treat depression.

1. Talk

If you are depressed, you may start to think negatively about yourself. Disappointment, sadness and anger can amplify your negative feelings. It often helps to talk about your feelings with family or friends. They will probably understand and want to support you. You can also contact specialized healthcare professionals. They can determine whether you suffer from depression and can offer you the right treatment.

2. Setting achievable goals

It is important that you keep achievable goals in mind. Try not to set too high standards for yourself, for example, that you must recover quickly or be able to do your work normally. In the beginning, it is best to focus on simple, everyday, practical activities. It takes time to process depressive emotions. It is important that you allow yourself that time.

3. Maintain regularity

Regularity helps. It is best if you go to bed and wake up at regular, regular times, and eat at regular times.

4. Avoid alcohol and drugs

Depression and substance abuse often coexist. That is why it is wise not to use alcohol and drugs.

5. To seek distraction

Distraction helps. It's good to get out and about in the great outdoors. Try to find activities that you find fun or relaxing.

6. Exercise and sports

Exercise is very important, even with depression. Walking, cycling, running or exercising for half an hour three times a week will help you feel less depressed. In addition, you will feel fitter and sleep better if you exercise regularly. Above all, choose a form of movement that you enjoy.

7. To work

If you succeed, try to keep working – even if it is only two half-days a week, for example. If necessary, discuss the options with the company doctor.

Post-traumatic stress

Post-traumatic stress disorder or PTSD is a psychological condition that can develop after experiencing shocking, traumatic experiences. Patients experience long-term psychological consequences of these experiences. PTSD has major consequences for daily functioning.

Symptoms

If you have PTSD, you suffer from anxiety, reliving, avoidance, tension and heightened alertness for more than a month. We describe these symptoms one by one.

Fear

You experienced a shocking event where you felt intense fear, helplessness or horror. The event is now over, but your fear remains.

Reliving

You regularly relive everything in your head. This often happens automatically, in one of the following ways:

- You have recurring thoughts about the event.
- You have nightmares.
- You always feel as if the event is happening again.
- You get confused if you see or hear something that reminds you of the traumatic event.
- You begin to tremble, sweat, or become paralyzed with fright when you see or hear anything that reminds you of the traumatic event.

Avoidance

- You avoid things that remind you of the traumatic event:
- You avoid thoughts, feelings and conversations about the event.
- You also avoid activities, places and people that remind you of them.

- You've repressed pieces, you can't remember them.
- You don't feel like doing things.
- You close yourself off from others. You feel like you don't belong anymore.
- You hardly talk about your feelings.
- You are gloomy about your future.

Tension and increased alertness

- You have become more irritable after the traumatic event. You feel tension. This is often accompanied by the following characteristics:
- You have trouble falling asleep or staying asleep.
- You are easily annoyed and have tantrums.
- You have concentration problems.
- You are overly vigilant and constantly on guard.
- You are scared and hypersensitive.

Tips

1. Take your feelings and complaints seriously

Accept that something is wrong. For example, start by keeping a diary. Writing can be a way to put into words what is on your mind. What are you afraid of? And what do you do then?

2. Talking breaths

Talk about what happened to you. This is very important for the processing process. You can talk to family or friends, but sometimes problems are easier to discuss with someone you know less well.

3. Pick up the daily routine again

Maintain a normal daily routine and eat healthily. Try to do something little by little.

See for yourself how you are doing and what you can handle. Give yourself time.

4. Find distraction in things you liked before

Look for distractions, do relaxation exercises or go for sports, such as cycling or walking. Also, take time to do 'fun things.

5. Seek expert help

Sometimes more help is needed than these tips. Then contact your doctor.

Aggression

Aggression is behaviour that someone uses to - consciously or unconsciously - destroy something, cause damage to another person, and/or make clear what he does or does not want. The behaviour exceeds the limits of what is generally acceptable in these situations and evokes feelings of fear, pain, sadness and/or anger in the other person.

We described aggression as life energy that people naturally possess and which they can use in many situations. However, we experience aggression mainly as transgressive, frightening and confusing behaviour. It often comes unexpectedly, so we feel overwhelmed by it; often we don't understand it either.

By learning more about aggressive behaviour and practising your reactions, you can better place, prevent and handle it.

What is anger?

Anger is a violent and aggressive type of emotion characterized by an increase in heart rate, blood pressure, and adrenaline and norepinephrine levels, with possible onset of sweating, redness, increased muscle tension, increased breathing, increased energy and gesticulation. Some see anger as part of the brain's response to the threat of an attack. Anger decreases the ability to reason.

It is a consequence of fear, lack of confidence, envy, jealousy, the fact that we do not know how to act, etc. It can also arise when we cannot control a certain situation, when we do not accept certain facts or when we are disturbed by the behaviour of others. In short, anger or aggression arises when we interpret a situation as a threat. They are often associated with feelings of fear, frustration, and even fatigue.

Personal problems or memories of traumatic events or situations that upset us can also trigger these types of emotions.

We feel frustrated about something, and that frustration sparks anger or rage.

Concretely, we can describe the chain as follows: expectations -> frustration -> anger and/or aggressiveness, aggression being the external manifestation of anger.

Anger is an emotion, and its nature makes it automatically triggered in certain situations, usually those that interfere with our goal. Like any emotion, it has a function: it prepares the body to make the effort necessary to overcome the obstacle that has arisen. It can present itself in various ways:

> Violent behaviour can be a means of achieving our goals when we cannot achieve them by other means: aggression is then instrumental. Behaviour is a lack of skills and can be improved by learning them.

> Anger can be like an overflow, the result of over-suppressing feelings that eventually make us explode for anything. In reality, we are also reacting to what has pissed us off previously. As our reaction seems disproportionate to us, we try to suppress it, which has the consequence of irritating us even more and generating an even more aggressive reaction. To get out of this

vicious circle, we must be able to react immediately to problems and frustrations by expressing them correctly and knowing how to deal with them. The reaction is adequate and measured because the reasons which push us to react are minor.

Aggression can also arise as a way of defending ourselves when we feel that there is an attack or a difficulty towards us (it is not always seen that way by others). This problem tends to occur when we react to the intentions of others rather than reacting to explicit facts. Judgment of intentions is the most frequent cause of our disproportionate violent reactions.

Anyone can get aggressive

Aggression arises not only in a person as an action or reaction to something he feels or thinks, but also in the interaction between people, or in the interaction between a person and the society in which he lives.

The safer, more at ease and relaxed a person feels, the more likely he is to relate to others calmly and pleasantly.

The opposite also applies: the more insecure, less at ease and tenser a person feels, the more likely he is to seek solutions that, in his view, nullify that insecurity and bring peace. In many cases, that is precisely the exertion of aggression yourself.

Aggression is destructive to the core and gives rise to its aggression: aggression breeds aggression, mistrust, suspicion and hatred. Aggression towards others and the other leads to alienation, loneliness and bitterness, because what else do you feel connected to?

Everyone can behave aggressively, but everyone handles that ability differently

How does it manifest itself?

Aggression can manifest itself in different ways:

> through emotions: rage, anger, indignation, revolt...
> through language (verbal aggression): hurtful words, insults, verbal attacks, harmful writings...
> through gestures of physical violence

through behaviours that flout common rules, which do not respect collective goods, which attack institutions ... (social violence) It can be directed towards oneself (risky behaviour, self-harm, suicide...), towards others, towards objects, towards animals or even towards institutions.

Tips

The best thing to do is to be aware of the situation. Aggression can be a response learned from childhood and the corona pandemic can trigger certain situations that give meaning to them, i.e. a child can learn to respond aggressively if this is what he observes.

Aggression is never (or almost never) the solution: being aggressive is to feel worse and make the problem worse.

You have to understand where the anger comes from and accept it as part of how human beings work to be able to control it. Find out why a person or situation makes you angry, and know that you cannot change the way others think, behave, or be where your frustration arises. We must understand that we will not be able to avoid these people or situations indefinitely: it is, therefore, better to assume them in part and work on what is within our reach: our way of reacting.

Specific techniques

Start by making a list of the situations that cause anger and aggression and see which you can avoid, usually very concrete situations (like stopping to watch the news or to read articles that you are not familiar with. 'agreement).

If the situation is inevitable, we must learn to deal with it:

1. Train yourself to detect the reaction of anger to act before it takes over your power: restless breathing, furrowed eyebrows, tight lips, very open or very closed eyes, clenched fists, sweating in the hands, increased heart rate. Be aware of your aggressive thoughts and feelings. The list of situations or people that make you angry will be useful for detecting reactions early and being alert to reactions.

2. If the anger takes hold, try to step away from the situation a bit to calm yourself down and avoid the outburst of aggression.

3. Get used to these situations, accept them as part of your daily life, of your life, and don't try to control them but rather understand your reactions to them. Our environment and the people around us are out of our control and we must accept it. To do this, you have to be in the present moment to understand what is happening, and not respond to past offences or problems that may arise in the future.

4. Cognitive reconstruction can be useful because it changes cognitive patterns (the way of thinking or perceiving things) leading to disproportionate and inappropriate thoughts facilitating the onset of anger. For example, we often think that others don't value us or waste our time, but attributing intentional actions to people only escalates the situation. We must avoid giving meaning to the behaviour of others, who do not do everything for the sole purpose of annoying us. These are everyday situations that we have to deal with.

5. Sometimes it can be helpful to put yourself in other people's shoes, as objectively as possible: how does this person rate our reaction? What made her react like this?

6. Expectations are one of the factors most associated with aggression. So avoid having too high expectations about others or situations. Everyone has different values and acts according to them, but we cannot wait for everyone to do the same.

7. Be aware of your interests in the various situations, as the impulsive behaviour becomes an emotional discharge which in reality does not allow us to achieve what we wish and sabotages our control of the situation.

What to do when you feel aggression coming?

Some exercises help distract our attention from the aggressiveness, from what we are feeling, and in regaining control. It's about diverting our attention from disproportionate thoughts and avoiding the aggressive response, replacing it with a more adaptive response. If the aggressive response is avoidable, the situation that causes it is inevitable, which is why we must train ourselves to do these techniques to automate them and they spontaneously take place when we get angry.

1. Count to 10 and do not speak until you have calmed down. You can also recite the alphabet backwards or think of something else. Breathe deeply and slowly several times.

2. Look for something to distract yourself: cleaning up, reading, watching a movie and picking up the problem once it calms down.

3. Expose yourself to the situation and analyze it as rationally as possible, think as someone else would, and consider alternatives to distorted thoughts that cause anger.

4. Make a list of phrases that calm us down and repeat them to ourselves during times of anger. Behaviour guides are also useful: decide that when something happens to you, you will then do such and such an action, regardless of how you feel. For example, if you are having a conversation with friends and you lose control, the conduct guide would say, "I am not in control of the situation, I apologize for my behaviour and express my desire to hand over the situation. conversation until later by expressing my disagreement while specifying that I respect the opinions of others ". If that doesn't work, find an excuse to walk away from the situation.

5. Meditation and relaxation techniques are very useful both in prevention and as a solution in times of anger.

All these techniques gradually make it possible to delay the aggressive response, and to no longer blindly obey the impulsive response, until it is controlled. You might have difficulty doing this at first, but even if you manage to get by for short periods or reduce the intensity of the anger, it's a success.

Insomnia

Insomnia (insomnia) is a sleep disorder in which you cannot sleep well and therefore do not have normal sleep, accompanied by functional problems during the day. You speak of normal sleep when you sleep five to ten hours. On average, you need about fifteen minutes to fall asleep. Waking up two to three times a night is normal unless it takes a long time to go back to sleep.

There are three types of insomnia. You have trouble falling asleep, you wake up often and/or you wake up too early. These three forms can also take place simultaneously.

In the world, at least 7% of people suffer from insomnia during the pandemic. In chronic insomnia, the symptoms occur three or more nights a week and last for more than three months.

Causes

A sleep disorder can be caused by various things, such as stress, lifestyle or traumatic events. The causes of apnea, narcolepsy and disturbances of the sleep-wake rhythm are often different.

Stress

Stress and tensions ensure that you are always alert. When you are tense, it is difficult to fall asleep. You can feel tension for many reasons: a high workload, worries about money or the upbringing of your children, relationship problems, etc.

Living habits

Lifestyle habits that make you sleep worse are smoking and drinking coffee or black tea. Nicotine, caffeine and theine are substances that keep you extra 'awake'. Also a lot of sugars (soft drinks), eating a lot of salt, eating too late or too much or going to bed without food make it harder for you to sleep. The same applies if you are still active late at night, such as playing sports or playing games behind the computer or email.

Traumatic Events

Traumatic events are, for example, an accident, burglary or the death of a loved one. This can cause sleep disorders, such as insomnia (chronic insomnia) and/or nightmares.

Age

Age also plays a role in sleep. Older people fall asleep less quickly and sleep less deeply. As you get older, you wake up more often and often have less need for sleep. This is because you do less and sleep more often in between. For example, if you try to sleep as long as you did when you were younger, you can develop sleeping problems.

In a vicious circle

If you suffer from insomnia, you will eventually get into a vicious circle. During the day you can concentrate poorly and you perform less. You often worry about this at night. You also increasingly dread going to sleep and you develop incorrect sleeping behaviour. For example, you always get out of bed at night. The fear of not being able to sleep only makes the stress worse and the sleeping problems worse. For example, a sleep disorder can continue to exist, while the original cause has long since disappeared.

Alcohol and sleep

Alcohol helps to fall asleep but also ensures light and restless sleep. If you drink alcohol, you wake up more often during the night and you don't feel rested in the morning. Do you often use a nightcap to fall asleep? Then you will notice that you need more and more alcohol to fall asleep.

Symptoms

Chronic insomnia has a major impact on your daily functioning. It is therefore a problem that bothers you twenty-four hours a day. Chronic insomnia can lead to:

- Reduced concentration
- Sleeping badly.
- Waking up frequently during the night (sleeping lightly/not sleeping well).
- Wake up early.
- Insufficient restorative sleep.
- Irritability
- Fatigue
- A lack of energy
- Emotional lability

When chronic insomnia persists for a long time, it can lead to depression and anxiety. The other way around is also possible: chronic insomnia can be the result of other psychological problems, such as depression.

Tips

If you suffer from insomnia, the tips below can improve your sleep. These tips are easy to try.

1. Relax before going to sleep

Do you still worry about your work when you're in bed? Or do you constantly list what you have to do tomorrow? It makes sense that you have a hard time falling asleep. If you want to fall asleep easily, you should completely relax a few hours before going to bed. A warm bath, a good book, your favourite song... help to shake off the stress. This way you are perfectly prepared for your sleep. Before you know it, you're dozing off.

2. Think about your sleep

Caffeine can also be the cause of poor sleep. Caffeine keeps you alert. Even if you drink a cup of coffee a few hours before bedtime, the caffeine is still in your body. Like alcohol, caffeine disrupts your sleep. You do not fall into a deep sleep and will therefore sleep badly.

Need a quick nightcap to sleep better? Better not though. Rather drink a cup of warm water. Oh yes, for the same reason as to why you should avoid alcohol and caffeine, it is best not to light a cigarette before going to bed.

3. Don't take your work to bed

It is better not to quickly check your e-mails or worry about work-related matters. Easier said than done. But that's how you make it difficult for yourself to sleep. Anyone who is still busy with work in bed becomes overwrought. That stress can lead to burnout. Try to push your work aside. Instead, spend time with your children or partner. Are you a real workaholic? Then think about what you still want to achieve. You are guaranteed to wake up smiling.

4. Turn off the blue light before going to bed

Do you still check your social media on your smartphone or tablet before going to sleep? Mobile devices produce 'blue light' and have a negative influence on the hormone melatonin. They give the impression that there is still light so that your eyes are less tired. You stay awake longer and your biological clock and sleep rhythm are turned upside down. Insomnia rears its head and you will be more tired the next day. It is, therefore, better to leave such devices in the living room.

5. Move at night

Exercise is also a good sleep tip. Too little exercise can cause sleeping problems. When you go jogging, you take the worries of the day away from you. In addition, a good condition reduces stress and you sleep better. So physical exertion promotes your sleep unless you do them right before going to bed. Your heart rate may still be too high, causing you to sweat and be restless.

6. Provide a pleasant temperature

A bedroom that is too warm or too cold can seriously disrupt your sleep. You fall asleep more difficult, sleep more restlessly and wake up faster. In general, it is best to sleep in a room where it is between 16 and 22°C. Of course, that depends from person to person.

Can't control the temperature in your bedroom? You can do something about the temperature in your bed. Synthetic materials usually do not ventilate very well, so you are often too hot in the summer. Or – worse – wake up soaked. Opt for natural materials as much as possible, such as a cotton cover (satin or flannel) and a down comforter. The fibres breathe, so they absorb and release heat. At the same time, they have an insulating effect. As a result, you never get too hot or too cold. This, in combination with a ventilating pocket spring or latex mattress and cotton pyjamas, ensures an ideal temperature throughout the night. Both in summer and winter.

7. Eat healthily

Do you like hearty food? Tasty! However, it is best to eat that heavy meal no less than two hours before bedtime. Although fats and sugars do make you sleepy, they disrupt your sleep. This is because your body needs a lot of energy to digest them. Are you still hungry in the evening? Go for a light meal.

8. Sleep in a bed that suits your body

In bed, your body recovers optimally from the efforts during the day. That is if your bed is tailored to your body and sleep needs. So have your sleep needs measured in a store. This way you know exactly where your body needs the most support. And you can – together with the sleep advisor – look for a bed in which you feel good. If you spend the night in a bed that is ergonomically composed, the risk of sleeping problems decreases and you wake up rested. Without back or neck pain, headache or shoulder pain. Good morning sunshine!

Paranoia

It is very difficult for someone with Paranoid Personality Disorder to relax and be open to interacting with others. People with this disorder are always anxious and wary, even if they have known someone for a longer period. They are constantly assessing the situation and are constantly looking 'the cat out of the tree'.

People with paranoid personality disorder always believe that others mean them badly. They look for something behind everything and are always afraid that other people will humiliate or disadvantage them. Contact with someone with a paranoid personality disorder is often problematic. Conflicts occur regularly. For that reason, it is difficult for someone with this disease to bind people to him. Support, protection and appreciation are rejected or approached with great suspicion. As a result, someone with a paranoid personality disorder often leads to an isolated existence.

Symptoms

Paranoia symptoms include:

- Suspecting others, without just cause, of exploitation, harm and deception
- Doubt the loyalty and trustworthiness of friends or colleagues
- Afraid of confiding in someone because of the unwarranted fear that information will be used against you

Even more paranoid personality disorder characteristics:

- Finding it hard to forgive someone when they insult you or say something unkind

- Find a disparaging or insulting meaning behind every innocent comment
- Feels unfairly attacked
- Doubts whether the partner is faithful

Paranoid Schizophrenia

Paranoid thoughts and behaviours make up a form of schizophrenia called paranoid schizophrenia. People affected by this type of paranoia commonly experience highly bizarre delusions or hallucinations, often about a particular subject. They often hear voices that others don't hear or think their thoughts are being controlled or broadcast aloud. In addition, the relationship with the family and in the work environment is deteriorating, and in many cases, without emotional expression.

What's the difference between paranoia and worry?

As stated, all people experience moments of paranoia. They see news about the increase in the number of deaths on TV or about a robbery in the neighbourhood and are afraid of being the next victim, so they start looking over their shoulder more often and checking for strange individuals in the neighbourhood before leaving the house.

This is a natural response to something that requires some kind of care, such as avoiding a robbery. In other words, it's an understandable concern that something might happen.

After a few days or weeks without new news of violence in the neighbourhood, people start to relax and, although they maintain a certain degree of attention, they still live their lives. The memory of the news disappears from his thoughts, returning only when someone mentions what happened.

But the excessive worry about the future turns into paranoia. The paranoid person is always thinking about "what if…?". What if I leave the house and something bad happens to me? What if I get the virus? What if I get mugged or kidnapped? What if someone I love gets hurt? As a result, they begin to sabotage their own life in an attempt to avoid these situations.

Tips

To curb paranoia, you need to change your mindset and the way you see life. Instead of putting so much energy into pessimism, why don't you try to see the good in the world and people? This may seem like cliché advice, but it's still effective.

Here are some tips on how to achieve this goal.

1. Fight Paranoid Thoughts

Bring your thoughts back to reality by practising simple exercises. One is to balance the most likely scenarios and the most unlikely ones.

Then think logically about them. What are the chances of that happening right now? How can you solve this problem if it happens? How can you prevent yourself? Fight paranoid thoughts with reason and reality, pointing out the flaws in your anxious reasoning.

2. Consume less harmful media

Completely avoiding the news about the country and the world is impractical. You need to know at least some information to make decisions, build a good way of life, and take care of yourself. After all, the news is a public utility and must be consumed!

However, if the exorbitant amount of negativity present in the media and social networks causes you harm, reduce consumption. See only what's relevant to your life and don't delve into morbid detail. If necessary, schedule a time to check the news, such as after work.

If you feel bad after consuming some kind of information, distract your mind with fun content or start a light conversation. That way you'll be able to control your mood.

3. Take a deep breath

When the shadow of fear or anxiety appears in your mind, breathe deeply. The act of taking a deep breath relieves tension in the body and stops the flow of chaotic thoughts. Then close the ruffles and inhale deeply a few times until your heart slows down. Only then return to your obligations.

4. Make plans, but don't get over them

You don't have to stop making plans to avoid anxiety and excessive worry. Planning is essential to reach your goals and have a life the way you idealize. So, make plans and have dreams yes!

What you can't do is cling to your plans as if they were life jackets. As life is made up of unforeseen events, inflexible people end up getting frustrated more often because their plans don't always work out. Embrace unpredictability as you try to carry out your plans.

The only things you can control are your reactions to events. This includes your emotions, words, thoughts and behaviours.

Emotional disorder

An emotional disorder is a change in a person's mental health, which leaves the person's well-being at a low. They are changes that occur in the functioning of an individual's mind, affecting their mood, reasoning, behaviours, attitudes, as well as performance, both in their personal and professional lives.

It is a type of problem that is so serious that it has become one of the main causes of disability and absence from work in our country.

The data that proves this is from the World Health Organization - WHO, which says that 12 million people suffer from depression and 18.6 million had anxiety because of the pandemic, which greatly increases our concern when it comes to emotional disorders.

Thus, we must be attentive and observe, not only ourselves but also the people around us, so that, in this way, we can help ourselves and contribute to the relief of pain for those who need it.

Tips

Of course, each case is different and the best option is to look for a specialized professional to help anyone deal with these and other emotional disorders that a person may experience.

However, some ways contribute for the symptoms of the emotional disorder to be truly alleviated. See what they are:

1. Healthy eating

Food has been shown to have a strong influence on our minds and emotions. Therefore, the tip here is that you invest in healthier eating, with foods rich in the nutrients you need in your body, in general, so that, in this way, you can take the first step towards a more emotional life balanced.

If by chance you have doubts about where to start, look for a nutritionist, because, for sure, this professional will have the ideal diet for your condition.

2. Physical activities

In addition to food, physical exercises are excellent allies in this process of improving emotional health, because, by practicing them, we are contributing to a series of well-being hormones being released in our body, which is essential for us to achieve feel much better to overcome the challenges of life.

3. Professional help

As we said above, the best way to deal with any types of emotional disorders is to seek expert help.

Look for a psychologist or psychiatrist, as they are the professionals best able to help you in this process of overcoming and restoring your emotional health.

So, look for this kind of help, so that, in this way, you can have, again, an even fuller life.

In addition to these disorders, there are many others. The important thing is not to know everyone, but to pay attention to the different attitudes of those around you, whether at work or outside of it. This person may need someone to talk to and encourage them to seek professional help.

By the way, this is another essential point. Never try to diagnose an emotional disorder on your own. There are health professionals who are specialized for this type of work. Always seek medical help.

Loneliness

In recent months, more attention and understanding has been given to the fact that young people also have to deal with loneliness. As the corona crisis lasts longer, more and more concerns are expressed about loneliness among young people and their social development.

Loneliness is not feeling connected. You lack a close, emotional connection with others. Or you have less contact with other people than you wish. Loneliness is a personal experience. Often it is a hidden problem. It is difficult for others to see from the outside if you are feeling lonely.

Lonely or alone?

Loneliness is not the same as being alone. For example, you can feel very connected to someone on the other side of the world, but you can also feel very lonely when you are surrounded by other people. So whether or not you are lonely depends on whether you feel a connection with others. When you don't feel a structural connection, you speak of loneliness. You lack a close, emotional connection or have fewer social contacts than you would like. This can make you feel empty, sad, anxious or redundant.

Therefore being alone or feeling lonely is not the same. It often coincides. When you are alone, you have no one around you. When someone has little or no social contact, we speak of social isolation.

Loneliness is different for everyone

What loneliness is, how it feels and what it does to you is different for everyone. Some need more meaningful relationships or a larger social network than others. It is impossible to tell whether people feel lonely. There is little talk about it. It can feel like your own failure when you're lonely. That is why it is good to be aware of signals that may indicate loneliness. Together we can discuss loneliness and do something about it.

Different kinds of loneliness

There are different kinds of loneliness. The main distinction made is between social loneliness and emotional loneliness. This concerns the number of contacts and the quality of the contacts respectively. Sometimes someone feels both, then it is also referred to as combined loneliness. The distinction between different types of loneliness is not only theoretical. It also requires a different approach.

Social Loneliness

This mainly concerns the lack of contact with people with whom someone shares certain common characteristics, such as friends, acquaintances or colleagues.

Emotional Loneliness

This occurs when a person lacks a close, intimate bond with one other person, usually the life partner.

Other 'types' of loneliness

In practice, you may also encounter other concepts. For example, existential loneliness, as a feeling of meaninglessness. Or chronic loneliness, if it lasts for a long time.

You are your own gauge

Loneliness is something you experience. This means that you are only lonely when you feel lonely. You are your own gauge. Loneliness is especially a problem for people who feel it strongly or for a long time. In short, when loneliness makes you unhappy or hinders your functioning.

Effects

Not only are people in poor health more likely to become lonely, conversely, loneliness also leads to poorer health. As a result, people can end up in a vicious circle, with serious consequences. Loneliness can have such a major impact on health that it is sometimes seen as the new smoking.

People who feel lonely are less happy and less satisfied with their lives. With prolonged loneliness, you can suffer from sleeping problems, stress and depression. It also increases the risk of Alzheimer's disease. If you are lonely, you are also more likely to smoke, drink and eat unhealthy foods. This puts you at a higher risk of obesity, high blood pressure and cardiovascular disease. Loneliness can even lead to suicide and premature death.

Tip to tackle loneliness

You can break through loneliness by reconnecting with other people. You can tackle this in different ways. Think, for example, of reviving 'old contacts' or participating in a group activity around a certain interest, hobby or sport where you can meet people. There are also buddy projects, where you can be linked to a 'buddy', usually a volunteer, with whom you can do something fun or have a chat. Young people also like to contact others via the internet, for example via a forum or social media.

If you don't know how to interact with others, for example how to have a chat or maintain a friendship, it can be useful to take a social skills training course.

Social foundation

Social relationships with other people such as relatives, friends and acquaintances are important 'resources' in everyday life. They form the 'social foundation' of every human being and contribute to the feeling of a meaningful life. A strong social network can also be a good buffer to prevent you from feeling lonely – for example at a later age.

Eating disorder

People with an eating disorder have disrupted eating behaviour that often has serious consequences for their mental and physical health. Everything that has to do with food is a source of tension for people with an eating disorder.

The cause of eating disorders is mainly psychological, but hereditary predisposition and environmental factors also play a role. A diet is of little use in an eating disorder.

Food is a constant source of tension and anxiety for these people. They have negative judgments about themselves, their body weight and their appearance.

Understanding an Eating Disorder

An eating disorder also known as Anorexia Nervosa can completely control you and prevents you from really being yourself. It is a complex, psychological illness that few really understand. Sometimes not even by the person himself, let alone by the outside world.

Because who can explain or make plausible the obsessive, dangerous and manipulative way of dealing with food and weight? In the mind of the (concerned) outsider, there are no plausible reasons to put your life on the line. It is simply difficult to empathize with the motivations of someone with an eating disorder.

The steps to recovery

Treatment for anorexia often begins when the need is high. At that point, it is most important that you regain your weight and that you understand the importance of treatment. Then you will work on your eating behaviour, physical recovery, recovery of your body experience, your self-esteem and the recovery of your social contacts.

1. Learn to eat healthily

The first step is to restore your weight to a healthy weight. Chances are that you will have to learn all about what a healthy diet is and how to stick to it.

2. Motivation to keep going

You will not only be motivated to eat healthily but also to complete your treatment. Incorrect thoughts and feelings about your eating disorder are often discussed. As a result, anorexia gets less and less of a grip on you.

3. Keep anorexia from coming back

The chances of anorexia coming back are quite high. So it is important to see where the disorder comes from in you. Psychotherapy is therefore always part of the treatment.

The real solution is not in 'normal' food or 'normal' weight. Sustainable recovery is about learning to look at yourself differently, from a more positive perspective. This is how you take the road (from falling and getting back up again) to more self-confidence and self-esteem. As a result, you no longer need the (non-)food to be able to deal with yourself, your environment and life. We believe in your strength and self-wisdom with which you hold the important key to get on the road to recovery.

Self-injury

Self-harm is an expression of psychological pain, anger or sadness. It means that you inflict injury or injury to your skin or body, without intending to end your life.

Forms of self-harm include cutting, scratching, scratching, burning, pulling hair, banging the head, ingesting harmful substances, or introducing objects into the body. Other terms you may come across in place of the term self-harm are "self-injury," "self-mutilation," "auto-aggression," and "self-mutilation."

Why does someone injure themselves?

The reasons behind self-injury are very diverse and different for everyone. Also, the "why" is often not completely clear to the person himself, making it difficult to explain this to others.

For example, the following reasons may occur:

- Discharge voltage;
- Expressing intense feelings;

- Reducing emotional pain by turning it into physical pain;
- As punishment or self-loathing;
- Wanting to feel something (with a feeling of emptiness, being numb, depersonalization, dissociation, etc.);
- Gain a sense of control or prove oneself: "I can bear this";
- Prevent worse (suicidal thoughts);
- Asking for attention and help, a signal to the environment: "I am not doing well".

In addition, self-injury is often perpetuated by the addictive effect. The pain releases endorphins in the brain, the "happiness hormone". This provides a short-term kind of relief. However, as with any other addiction, it takes more and more to achieve the same effect, and self-injury often increases in intensity over time.

You're not alone

Obviously, there is no simple answer to the question "what is self-injury". It can come from a lot of reasons, in a variety of people and in the form of different methods.

Figuring out the function of self-injury for you and looking for less destructive alternatives can be a long and difficult road, but it is not an impossible one. And you are not alone.

Suicide

Suicide is intentionally taking one's own life.

People who think about suicide often feel depressed, anxious, unhappy or alone for a long time. They may feel that no one understands them and no longer want to move on with their lives.

Myths about suicide

There are many myths about suicide and people who want to commit suicide. Many claims about suicide do not match reality. This has to do with misunderstanding but also with ignorance. Below is a summary several of fables, with the correct explanation:

Suicide is a disease

Reality: A suicide attempt is an expression of suffering, a cry of pain. A person with suicidal thoughts looks for a way out of a situation he or she considers intolerable and unsolvable. Suicidal behaviour in itself is not a disease. Certain psychiatric conditions such as depression and schizophrenia indeed increase the risk of suicidal behaviour. So sometimes suicidal behaviour can be related to or a consequence of a certain illness or psychiatric condition. In addition, our biological and genetic determination plays a role in the development of suicidal behaviour.

Suicide is hereditary.

Reality: Suicide is an extreme solution to a problem that is seen as unbearable and unsolvable. Often, someone who wants to commit suicide sees this as the only way out of an unlivable situation. When someone close to you commits suicide, it lowers the barrier to consider suicide as a solution. However, learned behaviour is not the same as hereditary behaviour. There is no specific suicide gene. It is true that some important risk factors (eg: biological risk factors, depression, alcohol abuse) can be partly genetically determined.

A suicide attempt is attention seeking.

Reality: About half of the suicide attempts are indicated by the person that he/she had a death wish. However, this does not mean that the suicide attempt in the other half is not serious. Very often there is a struggle between life as it is now and what they don't want and want another life without pain. Any attempt should be taken seriously, as previous suicidal behaviour is one of the greatest barriers to retrying. A suicide attempt is always a cry of pain and a signal that it cannot go on like this. Failure to respond to the situation is a lost opportunity to prevent an aggravation of the suicidal behaviour.

People who talk about it don't do it.

Reality: The vast majority (55-90%) of people who have died by suicide had given advance warnings. Talking about suicidal thoughts is an important signal that things are really not going well. Responding to these signals and discussing suicidal thoughts is, therefore, an important first step in trying to prevent suicide.

The improvement that follows a suicide attempt means the risk is over.

Reality: The majority of suicides happen in the first few months following an attempt. Although the person often seems to get a little better right after an attempt, this experience will lower the threshold for a next attempt in both the short and the longer term. It is important that someone is properly cared for after a suicide attempt and that it is determined what the person wants to achieve with this behaviour so that a new attempt can be prevented.

Suicide behaviour means the person wants to die.

Reality: The death wish is often ambivalent. However, a suicidal person usually does not want to die, often he or she simply sees no possibility to continue living in the current way. The desire for another life is often stronger than the desire to be dead.

A suicide happens impulsively.

Reality: A suicidal person goes through a whole process from thought to action that takes an average of 2.5 years. Biological, psychological, psychiatric and social aspects play a role in this. Often there is a drop that makes the bucket overflow. By bringing up the suicidal thoughts and death wishes, the suicide threat becomes visible and the suicidal process can be stopped in time.

Suicide is a normal reaction to an abnormal situation.

Reality: Suicide is an abnormal reaction to a normal situation: anyone can end up in stressful situations, but not everyone commits suicide as a result.

Dealing with suicidal thoughts

You want to control your suicidal thoughts, but you don't know how? Here are some tips for dealing with these thoughts and protecting yourself.

1. Watch out for signals

When you think about suicide, it often also has an impact on your behaviour. Therefore, be alert for changes in your behaviour that may indicate suicidal thoughts, such as sleeping poorly, spending less time with people, not being able to concentrate at work or school, worrying a lot about suicide, drinking more alcohol and/or smoking or no longer feeling like it. into things you otherwise enjoy.

2. Find a distraction

Sometimes it can help to try to shift your thoughts and avoid worrying. For example, by taking a walk, watching a movie, taking an extensive bath, playing sports or doing relaxation exercises. You can also do things with others without having to talk about your feelings. For example, going to play football with friends, have a drink with an old classmate or visit family.

3. Talk about it

While it may seem very difficult to talk to someone about suicidal thoughts, it can make all the difference. You can talk to someone close to you, such as a friend, family member, teacher or colleague.

4. Seek help

Staying alone with your suicidal thoughts is not a good idea. Know that you can always turn to help, both in your environment and from a professional counsellor.

5. Make a safety plan

Sometimes a situation seems so hopeless that you don't know what else to do. At such a moment, a safety plan can provide support. In this safety plan, you can keep track of what can calm you down in a crisis situation and who you can contact in case of an emergency.

6. Avoid alcohol and drugs

Stimulants and narcotics can lower the threshold for suicide because they affect your sense of perspective and can make you more impulsive or aggressive.

7. Do not look for dangerous places

Limit your access to places where you could attempt suicide as much as possible. Avoid being alone as much as possible and seek distractions.

8. Don't lock yourself up

Make sure that emergency services or other emergency personnel can easily reach you if necessary.

There were many psychological impact of the corona virus pandemic on the mental health of people but I've taken my time to explain a few common ones. If you suffered from any of the effects, the tips I gave will help you heal and get over them to recover your mental health.

I see you doing better.

CHAPTER 7

You and Your Mental Health

The increase in mental problems and their side effects have increased in recent years. This is a global trend, which is currently not seen as a global challenge due to lack of access to mental health care systems, both in high-income and low-to middle-income countries. Mental health problems also contribute to a large proportion of physical health problems, making it an even more important area of focus. Finally, global crises, such as the current pandemic, are accelerating the trend of increasing mental health problems. This shows how great the urgency is to take care of your mental health.

Don't give away your power

Strength is not about intimidating others or using aggression to get what you want. Power is about knowing that you are worthy enough to clearly and with confidence to ask for what you want. Because if you don't, the answer is almost always 'no'.

Perhaps people are also quite unclear when they talk about "giving away" their power.

1. You're chasing your dignity

Hunting for your dignity consists of pleasing, perfecting, pretending and proving. In other words, if you feel that you are not worthy of love and acceptance, you may find that you are excessively pleasing others by doing things you don't want or that you say 'yes' when you are actually 'no'. want to say. That's a good example of perfecting. Working very hard to try to make everything look good, hiding your feelings that may seem "messy", and trying hard to make the outside world think you are all right are all examples of things that can happen when you don't want to admit you're falling apart inside. By pretending, you may be saying that you're "fine" when it isn't at all.

2. You tolerate toxic relationships

Everyone has someone in their life who varies between not feeling quite well and completely draining your energy and your soul. This could be a family member, or a friend, a colleague or someone else. If you allow these people to behave toxically towards you, you are essentially giving them a part of you that is not being reciprocated. In other words, if you accept their toxic behaviour, you create an obstacle to the relationships you really want and deserve deep down.

3. You are very passive

Some people are naturally passive and if that's part of your personality, that can be a wonderful thing. But, if you don't stand up for yourself, you're giving away your power. You know, when you feel like someone has wronged you and you don't do anything about it. If you just take everyone's bullshit for granted, when you know you shouldn't. This often stems from fear and a lack of confidence.

4. You just let your dreams be dreams

You have dreams, just like everyone else. Maybe it's not to become the next big thing, but maybe it's that you want to be happier, or healthier. Whatever it is, if you sit and wish for it, and then say to yourself, 'But I can't, because...', you're cheating yourself. You give your power away to your inner critic. You pour it into your inner critic, as it were.

5. You are being manipulated

(Oh, oh, I have so much personal experience with this one). Manipulators have one goal: to control others to get what they want. How they do this varies from person to person (threatening, blaming you, humiliating you, and even flattery), but their goal is always the same. By not standing up for yourself, by not setting boundaries or by making up excuses for your manipulator, you are giving away your power.

6. You don't believe in yourself and/or you don't accept yourself

Being in control of your strength is influenced by how you feel about yourself. You can use how you feel as a yardstick to measure not only how much strength you have, but how you use your strength. Every time you give away your power, under any circumstance, you show yourself and the world that there is room for improvement when it comes to believing in and accepting yourself.

7. You allow your inner critic to make your choices

If your inner critic – or "gremlin" as I call it – is constantly in your head, you are giving away your power. Your gremlin wants you to fear the unknown, make you indecisive and hold you tight.

When you are mentally and emotionally empowered, you have more energy, less stress and you make your dreams come true more easily. People who are mentally and emotionally powerful share 13 common characteristics with which they manage their emotions, thoughts and behaviour. This leads to more success, more happiness and more joy. What exactly do they do that makes them mentally and emotionally strong, to be themselves and to put their passion into the world?

Successful people are no less afraid than others and have no less misfortune or more happiness. They only have the strength to get up and carry on.

Everyone who has achieved something in life has gone through deep valleys, has made mistakes, has fallen. But they pick themselves up and don't let it go. They continue in what they believe. They don't give up. They are emotionally and mentally powerful. As a result, they have the courage to follow their hearts, step into their greatness and put their passion into the world.

All of these people have 13 characteristics similar to what they do. Read on quickly and be inspired, so that you too become an expression of who you really are. So that you too follow your heart, step into your greatness and put your dreams and desires into the world. Because you are needed. You are there for a reason!

1: They do not feel they are victims of the circumstances.

They don't waste time on self-pity and don't step into the victim role. They are not concerned with fighting the circumstances. This costs a lot of negative energy and usually leads to powerlessness and frustration.

What do they do?

They take responsibility and set goals that are within their influence. They dare to look in the mirror and they understand that life doesn't have to be easy or fair. The moment you take responsibility for your life again, take responsibility for what you feel, then you are in your power and change is possible.

2: They don't give away their power.

They do not allow other people to have control or power over them. They don't say things like, "My boss makes me feel bad." We often blame others for our problems. Your parents didn't do things right, the government doesn't provide the right facilities, your partner left you, your best friend betrayed you, you don't have enough money or time to.... to do, and so on. The moment you do that you are not in your power and you give others the power over your life and your feelings

What do they do?

They understand that they are responsible for their thoughts and emotions. Another has power over you only if you give it to him. No one can make you feel inferior without your consent.

They know that they create their own thoughts and emotions.

If you believe in yourself, love yourself and value yourself, it doesn't matter what anyone else says. You experience what the other person says as feedback from which you can learn something, but it does not bring you down, you do not experience it as criticism. You will only be brought down if you don't believe in yourself, don't love yourself, don't value yourself and doubt yourself.

3: They are not afraid of change.

Many people find it difficult to let go of certainties. They are afraid that if they follow their heart that they do not earn enough money, that they have too little experience, that they cannot find a job because there is already so much unemployment or they are afraid of what other people say about it and do not dare to raise their heads. to protrude from the ground.

What do they do?

They welcome positive change and are flexible. They understand that change is inevitable and they believe in their ability to adapt. They look at the possibilities instead of the impossibilities. We tend to focus on worst-case scenarios. These people look at the best-case scenarios.

4: They don't waste energy on things they have no control over.

You don't hear them complaining about lost luggage, traffic jams and things like that. This takes a lot of energy while you do not influence it.

What do they do?

They focus on what is within their control. The only thing you can influence is the way you approach it, how you think about it. They approach every situation positively. They ask themselves the question: how does it get better than this? What else is possible? What can I learn from this experience? Despite the circumstances, what can I be thankful for?

5: They are not constantly trying to please or be liked.

Many people are afraid of being rejected, of not being liked, of not belonging. In doing so, they often go beyond their limits. Are they too quick to say yes to others and no to themselves? As a result, you lose energy, you take too much on your fork, you feel too responsible and you do things that you would rather not.

What do they do?

They dare to say no and stand up for themselves when necessary. They set clear boundaries. They do strive to be kind, friendly, and genuine, but they can handle it if people aren't happy with their choices.

6: They are not afraid to take risks.

Many people do not dare to take risks because they are afraid of failure. Fear of not being good enough. Some people are afraid of success, afraid to step into their greatness, afraid of being considered arrogant or being criticized. After all, tall trees catch a lot of wind? They do not dare to take the step into the unknown and cling to the certainties they now have. In the government, they also call this the golden cage. Civil servants have a good salary and above all good secondary conditions. This stops some officials from changing and taking risks to follow their hearts.

What do they do?

They take deliberate risks. They have courage, they dare to overcome their fear and carry on. Courage is not the absence of fear, but doing it despite the fear. They have the tools to overcome their inner critic and face their fears. They are not guided by limiting beliefs, they are guided by empowering beliefs.

7: They don't dwell in the past.

They waste no time thinking about how things could have been done better or differently. You cannot change the past.

What do they do?

They recognize their past and instead focus on what they have learned from their past. They know what talents and qualities they have developed thanks to their past. And they have faith in the future.

8: They don't hit the same stone twice.

They don't always do the same thing and expect a different result. As crazy as it sounds. That's what many people do. How often do you hear people say they want it different? And do they do something else? Mostly not. Many people continue to do the same, think the same and therefore feel the same. If you always keep thinking the way you thought, keep doing the way you always did, you'll keep feeling the way you've always felt and you'll always create the same result.

What do they do?

They avoid making the same mistakes over and over again. They learn from their mistakes and then make new choices. They believe that you always make the best choice you make at that moment and that a new choice is always possible.

They know that every choice has a consequence. They take full responsibility for this. Learn from it, and make a new choice.

9: They don't begrudge others their success.

They are not jealous or feel threatened when other people are successful or better than themselves.

What do they do?

They celebrate and appreciate the success of others. They know and recognize that success comes from hard work and dedication and they appreciate that. They are also willing to work hard for their success through dedication.

10: They don't give up after the first time.

They don't get discouraged if something doesn't work the first time. They don't give up. They don't see failure as a reason to give up right away.

What do they do?

They use their failure as an opportunity to grow and improve. They are willing to try until it works. They are convinced that there is no such thing as failure, there is only feedback.

Assuming this, "making mistakes" is no longer destructive or a failure, but then "mistakes" allow you to learn. You can compare it to a baby learning to walk. Before a child can walk, it falls several times. However, no parent doubts that their child is learning to walk. The parent picks up the child, comforts him, and encourages him to try again. Falling is part of the learning process. When in your life did falling become "failure"?

11: They are not afraid to be alone.

Many people are afraid of being alone, afraid of silence, afraid of being bored. They avoid this by looking outward in search of entertainment, such as computer games, television, shopping, going out. There's nothing wrong with that, of course, but if you avoid confrontation with yourself, it's very destructive.

What do they do?

They can tolerate silence and alone with their thoughts. They enjoy their own company and do not depend on others for happiness or entertainment. They use silences and being alone to reflect, contemplate, meditate in order to arrive at new insights and ideas.

12: They don't feel the world owes them anything.

We often look outside ourselves for happiness. If I have that job I will be happy. If only I had a relationship then I would be happy. If I have more money I will be happy. When I'm on vacation, I can finally relax. In this way, we make happiness dependent on what happens outside of us and we place the moment of happiness in the future. These people do not expect the world or others to make them happy. They do not seek happiness outside of themselves, they do not place the responsibility for their happiness on others.

What do they do?

These people create their happiness. To be happy you have to do something that makes you happy. They love themselves and they value themselves. They have compassion for themselves. They believe and trust in their potential to create and succeed.

13: They don't expect immediate results.

Everyone is in a hurry, everyone wants immediate satisfaction and immediate results. If that doesn't come soon, a lot of people will drop out or you'll get a bad rating. In organizations, it is very common not to sit in one workplace for more than four years. Executives and CEOs often want to bring about a complete change in those four years. When that change is there, they leave again. In this way, they are never confronted with the consequences of those changes. And there is a good chance that the next CEO or executive wants (or has to) leave his mark on a company in four years. While research has shown that it is much better for a healthy organization if CEOs and executives stay in place for ten years.

What do they do?

They are patient and give their efforts time to grow and blossom. Plants do not grow by pulling the leaves, but by watering the roots. Nature does not rush and yet everything is accomplished. Instant success takes 10 years. To be an expert at something, you need 10,000 hours of experience. This means 20 hours a week for 10 years.

Controlling your emotions

Controlling emotions is sometimes very difficult, sometimes you are very angry and you accidentally say something that was not intended. You often don't mean angry, but you just can't control your emotions. Many people will understand that it all became too much for you, but this is not the case for everyone. It is therefore important that your emotions do not completely take over, but that you can keep the emotions under control. There are also different emotions that all have different effects on you, so the emotions such as anger and fear can protect you at certain times. Some emotions are a lot less useful, such as jealousy. Because of jealousy you only have yourself, because you compare yourself with others and that is not the intention.

Many people think that keeping your emotions under control means that you can't or shouldn't show the emotions anymore, but that's not the case. It doesn't mean that you are going to ignore or hide your emotions, you have to surrender to them to take control of them.

Emotions are powerful

Your mood determines how you interact with the people around you. Are you grumpy? Then you are logically not at your best. Have you had a wonderful morning and are you very happy? There is a good chance that your colleagues or the bakery on the corner can expect a big fat smile.

But emotions do more, and this one was hard to swallow when I first read it. Because emotions also affect how much you spend. Are you stressed?

For some people, this manifests itself in shopping. Or just when you're happy, you can suddenly be much more generous to yourself and others because, f*ck it - you're happy! Your mood determines what you spend your time on and how you deal with challenges.

When you get your emotions under control, you can handle a lot more mentally. Just imagine: you haven't been touched by the slightest thing that makes you catty to your loved ones? Or do you not feel threatened when your partner has sex with someone else? You are not afraid to do something, but just go for it? That would be a relief for you and those around you.

Take control of your emotions

Emotions, how do you control them? Whoever controls his emotions has control over his life. Emotional mastery is the key to a life you lead. The ability to control what you feel in every moment is one of the most important skills you can have. Three forces determine what you feel. We call these three together 'Emotional Triad'. Together these three determine every, and every emotion.

What you feel is not something you feel automatically!

You feel what you feel because you have chosen this with your 'Emotional Triad'. To control your emotions and consciously choose the emotions you live with daily, you need to understand these three forces and know how to use them to your advantage.

1: Physiology

Emotion is created by movement. What you feel right now is directly related to the way you move your body. If you slump your shoulders and lean your head forward, you will soon depart into a state of depression. So, the next time you feel a little depressed, stand up, throw your shoulders back, and take a few deep breaths. You will see that it makes you feel in a different frame of mind. You see possibilities again and you will make faster and better decisions. You will feel stronger and enjoy a sense of self-confidence while keeping an overview of the unpleasant situation you may find yourself in. Weird? Try it! You will see that it works!

2: Language

Language comes in many forms. Also in the form where you have to ask yourself questions, either out loud or in your head. If you ask yourself, "Why does this always happen to me?" You will experience a very different set of emotions than if you created early, "How to take advantage of this situation?" Or "Where is my present in this situation?" Or "What's humorous about this?" Remember that the secret of the top coach is to ask the questions that the coaché doesn't ask himself! The language patterns you use play an important role in the meaning you give to the same situation With different words, the same situation gets a different meaning for you And... with that the same situation, but now with a different meaning, gives you other emotions too! The next time you find yourself in a situation where negative emotions threaten to take over. Then look at the language you are currently using. How can you, by communicating with yourself differently, shift your emotions and create more of a sense of empowerment?

3: Focus

Energy flows to where you put the focus. Everything that gives you focus, attention, grows. In other words, your life is governed by what you focus on. That's why you should focus on where you want to go, not on what you fear. When you find yourself in an emotional state of uncertainty, resist your fear. Shift your attention to where you want to go and your actions will take you in that direction. Understanding how to influence your 'Emotional Triad' and applying the tips above are the first steps to using your 'Emotional Triad' to control your emotions to your advantage. When you manage to influence your emotions, you will spend more time in positive emotions. Positive emotions empower you and let you make decisions and actions that bring out the maximum in you and enjoy every moment of your life.

A healthy self-esteem

In short, self-esteem is the value you place on yourself, the opinion you have about yourself and your abilities. While everyone occasionally has self-doubts, what is commonly known as low self-esteem breeds insecurity and general dissatisfaction.

When self-esteem is healthy, we not only feel better about ourselves, we are also more resilient. Studies show that when self-esteem is healthy, we are likely to experience common emotional wounds, such as rejection and failure, as less painful and recover from them more quickly. We are also less vulnerable to anxiety; we release less cortisol into our bloodstream when we are under stress and it is less likely to remain in our system.

Low self-esteem is, unfortunately, a self-fulfilling prophecy. The worse you feel about who you are and what you do, the less motivation you will have to do whatever it takes to build your self-esteem.

From there, it's easy to spiral down into a circular, negative thinking cycle, keeping you stuck in harmful – and erroneous – beliefs.

Breaking this vicious cycle and starting to move in a more positive direction is a process and won't happen overnight, but there are things you can do to get it started and keep it moving. You may be able to identify some things that are affecting your opinion of you (you may be bullied or feeling lonely), or many other possible factors. Anyway, if you're wondering how to improve your self-esteem, here are some of our top tips:

Increase your self-esteem

1. Disconnect your self-esteem from others

Yes. If you let your self-esteem depend on other people, it will be difficult to maintain it. Self-esteem must come from within yourself. It's about the bond you have with yourself. If you only experience self-esteem when someone approves you, then you live without a runway, and you will get a lot of cow shit in your face.

Sorry – but that's just the way it is.

So? So realize that increasing your self-esteem is your own responsibility. And that you are the only one who can develop it.

What you want to do is – in small steps – increase your self-esteem by proving to yourself that you are more valuable than you now believe. And I know — there are easier things in the world. But life doesn't always have to be easy.

So let's see what steps we can take.

2. Observe your self-criticism

You are unkind to yourself. And that has to stop. Because it is your thoughts about yourself that determines your self-esteem. And if you think less of yourself then — well — let's just say it doesn't bring many positives.

You feel inferior because you think inferior thoughts. Things like:

"I can not do that."

"They don't want me in their group anyway."

"That's not for me."

"I'm not good enough."

"I'm a loser, and everyone sees it."

"I'm not pretty enough to talk to that person."

"Everything I do fails."

"I have only bad luck and misery."

I don't know about you - but it gives me the creeps just reading it. What a misery.

And yet it is these kinds of thoughts that keep your self-esteem stuck at a low level. They are poisonous thoughts that are untrue, unreasonable and unkind.

So? So you want to delete them. And you want to turn them into better thoughts. Thoughts that support your self-esteem and give you a little less cow shit. Thoughts such as:

"I'm fine the way I am."

"If I do my best I can do this."

"I know that I am valuable as a friend."

"If something fails, I can learn from it and try again."

"Even if I fail, I'm still a good person."

"I'm quite a nice person."

"I deserve respect, love and compassion. Also from myself."

Doesn't this feel much better? Anyway – how do you do this? Yes, you can just repeat these more positive thoughts throughout the day as a sort of mantra. And you will get results with that.

3. Take positive steps towards more self-esteem

Okay. So you realize that you have to get your self-esteem out of yourself. And you have begun to observe and transmute those toxic thoughts. What else can you do to avoid it?

Everything.

You can take a lot of small, positive steps. Do things that make you feel more valuable. Because when you achieve things, you prove to yourself that you can get things done.

Depending on where you are in your life, these small steps can look very different.

You can start getting your life together. Start cleaning, repairing, cleaning and minimizing. So that you have a pleasant base.

You can cut responsibilities and projects that make you unhappy from your life. By getting rid of them, or by completing them to get rid of them.

You can challenge yourself to break a negative habit. Such as using too many substances, spending hours on your smartphone or eating unhealthy foods.

You can take steps to get your finances in order. So that more comes in than goes out.

You can exercise more and eat healthier so that you feel better about yourself.

You can challenge yourself to take up a new project – and move forward very consciously with self-love and self-compassion.

You can keep a journal, and write down what's going on in your head. So that you can view those negative thoughts objectively and let them go.

4. Feel acceptance and forgiveness for yourself

Once you have a better idea of who you are, the next step is to increase your acceptance of yourself.

Start by forgiving yourself for everything you noticed in certain questions above; think about any struggles, need for perfectionism, mistakes and bad habits you may have and give yourself a moment to forgive and accept yourself without judgment or excuses.

Think about everything you learned about yourself in the first exercise and repeat these statements:

I accept the good, the bad and the ugly.

I fully accept every part of myself, including my mistakes, fears, behaviours, and qualities that I may not be too proud of.

This is how I am, and I'm okay with that.

5. Improve your self-love

Now that you've worked on accepting yourself for who you are, you can start building love and care for yourself. Make it a goal to increase kindness, tolerance, generosity, and compassion for yourself.

To stimulate your self-love, start looking at your internal dialogue – with yourself! Make it more positive and uplifting when you talk to yourself.

If you're not sure how to get started, use these simple sayings:

I feel valued and special.

I love myself.

I am a dignified and capable person.

As I said – there are endless small positive steps you can take to develop more self-esteem. And every small step forward is one.

Just start somewhere.

Today, preferably now.

Do something small to make your life a little better, to contribute something, to do your future self a favour. You don't have to do it all at once – just do something.

From there you can start an upward spiral. Combined with daily meditation you will notice that your self-esteem grows slowly but surely. And that life begins to smile at you.

Mental strength

Some people seem to have everything right while others continue to struggle. What makes the difference between the two types of people?

The right mindset and mentality.

Your thoughts determine your feelings. The better you feel, the easier it becomes to work more productively. You feel better about yourself, smile more and reach your goals faster.

The bridge between dreaming and doing is your mindset. Developing your mental strength helps you to create a positive mindset. But how do you do that?

Developing mental strength

You train your mental health by paying more attention to your thoughts. Just like training your body, it is important to maintain your mindset. You can apply the following tips:

Tip 1: Start your day with positive thoughts

What are you thankful for today? What beautiful things are you going to do today? Write in a few sentences what you are grateful for.

Tip 2: Make your agenda sacred

You can only do that by deciding for yourself what will be on your agenda. If you don't plan for your own life, you will be lived by the plans of others. Be prepared so you can anticipate what others want from you.

Tip 3: Don't plan anything in the morning

The morning is currently where we can work fully focused on what we are doing. So, as far as possible, do not plan external appointments. Work on your most important task in the morning.

Tip 4: Write everything down

Act like a student who wants to know everything. This is a good way to develop mental strength.

This way you can optimally use your thoughts for other tasks. Focus.

Tip 5: Don't be guided by the news

We receive messages, emails and other external stimuli such as the news at any time of the day. Ask yourself: did I choose to read this news or did it just happen to me?

Tip 6: Develop more mental strength by strengthening your willpower

Compare our energy level to a battery. This one runs out the more we use it. That's how it works with our willpower. We cannot change everything at once. A change costs energy and that drains our battery.

Tip 7: Recharge your mental energy

Did you use a lot of willpower in one day? Then charge your battery again. Relaxation time is important. Get enough sleep, do fun things and take time for yourself.

Tip 8: Change your thoughts

Negative thoughts remain in our brains two to three times longer than positive thoughts. They have a greater influence on our lives.

It is wise to consciously look for more inspiration around you. This way you develop more positivity for more mental strength.

Tip 9: Your body and mind sometimes need an energy boost to make you grow as a person

Take on the challenge and peak at the right time. Maybe you want to be able to meditate for an hour at a time? Running a marathon? Starting your own business? Give yourself a big challenge at least once a year.

Tip 10: Developing mental strength is only possible by having the right focus

Make your goals clear and clear so that you know for sure what you want and where you want to go.

Develop sustainable mental strength

These short powerful tips have a direct effect on developing your mental strength. You simply receive mental strength by applying several habits. The trick is to gain insight into your own actions and to respond to them.

Training and developing your mentality may seem simple. It also takes a lot of time, patience and discipline to set this up.

Don't allow the pandemic get a toll on your mental health.

You can scale through.

Get to work.

REFERENCES

Medrxiv. (2020). Distress among Brazilian university students due to the Covid-19 pandemic: survey results and reflections. Retrieved from https://www.medrxiv.org/content/10.1101/2020.06.19.20135251v1

Rentokil. (2021). Important Coronavirus information update. Retrieved from: https://www.initialcaribbean.com/about-initial-hygiene-caribbean/coronavirus/

Center for Disease Control and Prevention. (2021). Frequently Asked Questions. Retrieved from: www.cdc.gov/coronavirus/2019-ncov/faq.html

Jama. (2020). Characteristics of and Important Lessons From the Coronavirus Disease 2019 (COVID-19) Outbreak in China. Retrieved from: jamanetwork.com/journals/jama/fullarticle/2762130

Lisheng, W., Yiru W., Dawei Y., and Qingquan L., (2020). Review of the 2019 novel coronavirus (SARS-CoV-2) based on current evidence. Retrieved from:

www.ncbi.nlm.nih.gov/pmc/articles/PMC7156162/

Alexander, F. (2020). Coronavirus: Everything you need to know. Retrieved from: www.dw.com/en/coronavirus-everything-you-need-to-know/a-52102486

Center for Disease Control and Prevention. (2021). COVID-19, MERS & SARS. Retrieved from: www.niaid.nih.gov/diseases-conditions/covid-19

Christie, F., (2018). What is the importance of mental health?. Retrieved from: https://www.queenshealthemporium.com/what-is-the-importance-of-mental-health/

Umcg. (2021). Study with Lifelines data into the transmission of the coronavirus within households. Retrieved from: https://umcgresearch.org/w/study-with-lifelines-data-into-the-transmission-of-the-coronavirus-within-households

Umcg. (2021). Influence of DNA on behaviour and wellbeing during coronavirus pandemic has increased. Retrieved from: https://umcgresearch.org/-/influence-of-dna-on-behaviour-and-wellbeing-during-coronavirus-pandemic-has-increased

Rug. (2021). Our scientists and the corona crisis. Retrieved from: https://www.rug.nl/research/corona-publicaties/?lang=en

Dc papers. (2021).Special forms of depression - Everything about it. Retrieved from: http://www.dc-epaper.com/special-forms-of-depression-everything-about-it/

Made in the USA
Coppell, TX
19 October 2022